WALLACE COLLECTION

# SUMMARY
# ILLUSTRATED
# CATALOGUE
# OF PICTURES

THE TRUSTEES OF THE WALLACE COLLECTION,
MANCHESTER SQUARE,
LONDON W1M 6BN

1979

Printed and bound at William Clowes & Sons Limited
Beccles and London

# PREFACE

It is anticipated that stocks of the partially-illustrated 1968 *Catalogue of Pictures and Drawings* will soon be exhausted. Both content and presentation now stand in need of revision, and a completely new catalogue is planned in three volumes (1 *British, Italian and Spanish; 2 French; 3 Dutch and Flemish*). This will take time, and the present *Summary Illustrated Catalogue* is designed to help fill the gap before the new volumes begin to appear. It is intended to provide a handbook for visitors as well as a summary of research since 1968; the format is modelled on the National Gallery's *Shorter Illustrated Catalogue* of 1973. Some recent monographs and articles of outstanding importance are listed under the artists or pictures concerned; some older reference works are quoted in order to correct or complete essential information (e.g. Hofstede de Groot). A list of renamed attributions is appended, together with a numerical index.

Many scholars have contributed, indirectly, to this volume; some are named in the text, but many others may recognise their opinions reflected in summary form. I would like to declare my indebtedness and to thank them. Ruth Cowell assisted me in the preparation of the text, which was read by both Terence Hodgkinson, my predecessor, and Robert Cecil, my former colleague. I am most grateful for their assistance.

February, 1979

JOHN INGAMELLS
Director

# INTRODUCTION

The majority of the pictures were acquired between 1841 and 1870 by the 4th Marquess of Hertford, in London and Paris. His father had previously acquired the Titian, *Perseus and Andromeda*, and some distinguished Dutch pictures. Between 1871 and 1886 Sir Richard Wallace added some 16th-century pictures with others more in his father's taste. The collection contains nearly eight hundred items, and is particularly renowned for its 18th-century French paintings and the 17th-century European masters. In more general terms, it is enjoyed for the way it reflects the instincts of wealthy and knowledgeable amateurs, who bought for pleasure.

Hertford House, the home of the Wallace Collection, was built between 1776 and 1788 as Manchester House for the 4th Duke of Manchester. It was acquired by the 2nd Marquess of Hertford in 1797. After his widow's death it served as the French Embassy from 1836 to 1850, and it was then used by the 4th Marquess of Hertford as a picture store. In 1871 Sir Richard Wallace who, like his father, had been living in Paris, decided to make it his principal London residence and he promptly renamed it Hertford House and made considerable alterations to accommodate the collection. Further modifications were made between 1897 and 1900 so that the House could become a public museum. It was opened as a National Museum by the Prince of Wales on 22 June 1900.

# THE SEYMOUR-CONWAY FAMILY, EARLS and MARQUESSES of HERTFORD

## Founders of the Wallace Collection

Francis Seymour-Conway (1719–94; Earl of Hertford & Viscount Beauchamp 1750; Earl of Yarmouth & *Marquess of Hertford* 1793)   m. 1741 Lady Isabella Fitzroy (1726–82) d. of 2nd Duke of Grafton

seven sons and six daughters, of whom

Francis Ingram Seymour-Conway (1743–1822; Viscount Beauchamp 1750; Earl of Yarmouth 1793; *2nd Marquess of Hertford* 1794)   m. 1. 1768 Alice Elizabeth (d. 1772) d. of Viscount Windsor
2. 1776 Isabella Anne Ingram-Shepherd (1760–1834) d. of 9th Viscount Irvine

only surviving child

Francis Charles Seymour-Conway (1777–1842; Viscount Beauchamp 1793; Earl of Yarmouth 1794; *3rd Marquess of Hertford* 1822)   m. 1798 Maria Fagnani (1771–1856)

two sons and one daughter, of whom

Richard Seymour-Conway (1800–70; Viscount Beauchamp 1800; Earl of Yarmouth 1822; *4th Marquess of Hertford* 1842)

one illegitimate son
(by Mrs. Agnes Jackson, c. 1789–1864)

Richard (Jackson) Wallace (1818–90; name changed to Wallace 1842; Baronet 1871)   m. 1871 Amélie Julie Castelnau (1819–97)

Lady Wallace bequeathed the major part of
the family's collection of works of art to
the Nation as The Wallace Collection

# EXPLANATION

*Attributions:* a picture is considered to be by the artist named unless the name is qualified: the terms *imitator* and *manner of* are self-explanatory, but the following may require comment:

*after*   copy or adaptation of
*ascribed*   formerly thought to be by, but now doubted
*attributed*   probably by
*follower*   by an artist in the circle of
*studio*   by assistants, probably with help from the artist
*workshop*   an earlier term for *studio*

Measurements are given in centimetres, height before width

Where no date of acquisition is given, the first certain reference to the picture in The Collection is in the Bequest of Lady Wallace, 1897.

*Abbreviations*
b.   born
bap.   baptised
c.   *circa*, about
d.   died
HdG   C. Hofstede de Groot, Catalogue raisonné of the works of the most eminent Dutch painters of the Seventeenth Century, 10 vols., 1907–28
m.   married
RA   Royal Academy
s   signed
sd   signed and dated

# Andreas ACHENBACH
## 1815–1910

b. Kassel, d. Dusseldorf; worked in Dusseldorf, painter of sea and coast scenes.

**P618   THE EBB-TIDE**

Signed: *A. Achenbach 1849*

Panel 46·0 × 68·3

Acquired by 1872

P618

# Francesco ALBANI
## 1578–1660

b. and d. Bologna; worked in Rome and Bologna, a pupil of the Carracci Academy.

**P642   VENUS AND AMORINI**

Copper 29·8 × 39·7

The composition recalls Albani's emblematic group of *Fire* which appears in both his *Allegory of Fire* (Turin) and *Winter* (Paris art market 1920).

Purchased by the 4th Marquess of Hertford 1849

P642

# Heinrich von ANGELI
## 1840–1925

b. Oedenburg, Hungary; Court portrait painter, worked in London, Vienna, Munich and St. Petersburg.

**P577   THE EMPRESS FREDERICK as CROWN PRINCESS**

Signed: *H. von Angeli 1882*

Canvas 71·1 × 57·8

Victoria Adelaide Mary Louisa (1840–1901), eldest child of Queen Victoria and Prince Albert, m. 1858 Prince Frederick Hohenzollern, later Crown Prince of Prussia and German Emperor in 1888; mother of Kaiser Wilhelm II.

Presented by the sitter to Sir Richard Wallace

P577

# Jacob Adriaensz BACKER
## 1608–1651

b. Haerlingen, Friesland, d. Amsterdam; pupil of Rembrandt, painter of portraits and histories.

P89

### P89   AN OLD WOMAN

Inscribed: *Aet. 69*

Canvas 121·3 × 97·8

Falsely inscribed on chair arm *Rembrandt f. 1632* (partially removed in cleaning 1976). An uninscribed version is in a Dutch private collection.

Acquired by 1872

# Ludolf BAKHUIZEN
## 1631–1708

b. Emden, d. Amsterdam; pupil of A. van Everdingen, q.v.; worked mainly in Amsterdam.

P244

### P244   SEA PIECE

Signed: *L. Bak..* and *L.B.*

Canvas 53·3 × 75·6

(HdG 239)

P248

### P248   SHIPS IN A STORM

Signed: *L.B.*

Canvas 52·7 × 61·9

(HdG 240)

Acquired by 1872

# Domenico BECCAFUMI, attributed to
## 1486(?)–1551

b. and d. Siena where he chiefly worked (E. Baccheschi, *Opera completa di Beccafumi*, Milan 1977)

### P525  JUDITH WITH THE HEAD OF HOLOFERNES

Panel 85·1 × 47·9

P525

The subject is taken from the Apocrypha, *Judith* xiii, 6–10. Two paintings from the same series, *Sophonisba* and *Cleopatra*, are in the Musée Bonnat, Bayonne. (Baccheschi 201, attributed)

Purchased by Sir Richard Wallace 1872

# Joseph-Louis-Hippolyte BELLANGÉ
## 1800–1866

b. and d. Paris; pupil of Gros, q.v.; Keeper of the Rouen Museum 1837–54.

### P581  CROSSING THE FORD

Signed: *h^{te} Bellangé*

Canvas 54·3 × 72·7

Acquired by 1872

P581

### P586  THE IMPERIAL TENT

Signed: *h^{te} Bellangé 185[9?]*

Panel 45·7 × 38·1

Acquired by 1872

P586

P620

### P620   THE DESPATCH

Signed: *h$^{te}$ Bellangé 1845*

Panel 38·1 × 46·4

Purchased by the 4th Marquess of Hertford 1845(?)

P650

### P650   THE SOLDIER'S FAREWELL

Signed: *h$^{te}$ Bellangé 1829*

Water-colour 19·7 × 22·5

Acquired by 1874

P671

### P671   NAPOLEON AT WATERLOO

Signed: *h$^{te}$ Bellangé 1836*

Water-colour 42·2 × 33·7

Acquired by 1872

P683

### P683   NAPOLEON AND HIS STAFF

Signed: *h$^{te}$ Bellangé 1839*

Water-colour 40·3 × 28·9

Acquired by 1872

**P705 THE FAREWELL**
Signed: *h^{te} Bellangé 1859*
Water-colour 22·9 × 19·1
Acquired by 1874

P705

**P720 THE FRENCH AT BRUGES**
Signed: *h^{te} Bellangé 1833*
Water-colour 33·3 × 46·4
Acquired by 1874

P720

**P730 A GRENADIER**
Signed: *h^{te} Bellangé 1830*
Water-colour 16·5 × 13·3
Acquired by 1872

P730

**P742 MILITARY COURTSHIP**
Signed: *h^{te} Bellangé 1829*
Water-colour 7·9 × 6·7

P742

**P748 WATERLOO**
Signed: *h^{te} Bellangé*
Water-colour 10·5 × 14·0
Acquired by 1872

P748

# BENVENUTO DI GIOVANNI, attributed to
## 1436–after 1509

Pupil of Vecchietta, worked in Siena.

P543

### P543   SAINT JEROME

Panel 32·4 × 21·9

The Saint is shown beating his breast with a stone, the lion lying by his side. Probably part of a dismembered predella.

# Nicolaes BERCHEM
## 1620–1683

bap. Haarlem, d. Amsterdam; studied in Haarlem and Amsterdam, noted for his Italianate landscapes.

P25

### P25   THE OLD PORT OF GENOA

Signed: *Berchem*

Canvas 84·5 × 104·8

Painted *c.* 1658, showing the influence of J. B. Weenix, q.v. A repetition, with variations, is in the Kunsthalle, Hamburg. (HdG 78)

Acquired by 1872

P183

### P183   THE FERRY BOAT

Signed: *Berghem 1672*

Panel 33·0 × 38·1

(HdG 194)

Acquired by the 3rd Marquess of Hertford by 1834

**P185 LANDSCAPE WITH CATTLE**

Signed: *Berchem*

Panel 33·3 × 44·1

(HdG 195)

Acquired by the 4th Marquess of Hertford by 1859

P185

**P186 ITALIAN LANDSCAPE WITH FIGURES**

Signed: *C P Berghem f. 1654*

Canvas 54·6 × 65·4

(HdG 498)

Acquired by 1872

P186

**P213 HALT AT AN INN**

Signed: *Berchem f.*

Canvas 50·8 × 41·3

(HdG 142)

Acquired by 1872

P213

**P256 JUPITER WITH THE NYMPHS ON MOUNT IDA**

Signed: *C P Berghem 1654*

Canvas 64·5 × 85·7

The infant Jupiter is being fed by the goat Amalthea. (HdG 43)

Acquired by 1872

P256

P640   **THE MUSICAL SHEPHERDESS**

Signed: *Bergh.. 1658*

Copper 34·0 × 41·9

(HdG 251)

Purchased by the 4th Marquess of Hertford 1848

P640

# Francesco de BIANCHI FERRARI, ascribed to
## *c.* 1460–1510

b. and d. Modena; pupil of Tura(?) and follower of Ercole Roberti; there are few certain works by him.

P2   **DAPHNIS AND CHLOE**

Panel 86·4 × 62·5

The subject is taken from Longus, *Daphnis and Chloe*, a pastoral romance from antiquity. After being attibuted to Bianchi Ferrari by Claude Phillips, P2 was attributed to G. B. Bertucci by Berenson.

P2

# Giovanni BILIVERT, after
## 1576–1644

b. and d. Florence; pupil of Cigoli, influenced by Caravaggio.

P643   **TARQUINIUS AND LUCRETIA**

Copper 24·4 × 30·8

The rape of Lucretia by Sextus Tarquinius (cf. Shakespeare's *The Rape of Lucrece*). A much reduced copy from a painting in the Accademia di San Luca, Rome, attributed to Bilivert.

Acquired by 1872

P643

# Louis-Léopold BOILLY
## 1761–1845

b. La Bassée (Nord), d. Paris; painter of genre scenes, a regular exhibitor at the Salon from 1791.

### P435    THE DEAD MOUSE

Canvas 41·3 × 32·4

Acquired by 1872

P435

### P473    THE VISIT RETURNED

Canvas 45·1 × 55·6

According to a label, *verso*, painted in 1789.

Purchased by the 4th Marquess of Hertford 1863

P473

### P479    THE SORROWS OF LOVE

Canvas 45·1 × 55·6

According to a label, *verso*, painted in 1790.

Purchased by the 4th Marquess of Hertford 1863

P479

# Ferdinand BOL
## 1616–1680

b. Dordrecht, d. Amsterdam; pupil of Rembrandt in Amsterdam in the later 1630s.

P74

### P74 THE TOPER

Signed: *F. Bol*

Canvas 91·4 × 84·5

Probably from the 1640s.

Acquired by the 4th Marquess of Hertford by 1859

# Attributed to BOL

P78

### P78 A YOUNG WOMAN

Canvas 81·3 × 65·1 oval

Probably painted *c*. 1640. Formerly attributed to Flinck, q.v., but not accepted as such by von Moltke who suggested the present attribution. (von Moltke, *Flinck*, p. 251, no. 122)

# Marie-Rosa BONHEUR
## 1822–1899

b. Bordeaux, d. Chateau By, Fontainebleau; she achieved considerable fame as an animal painter.

P260

### P260 A WAGGON AND TEAM OF HORSES

Signed: *Rosa-Bonheur 1852*

Canvas 34·9 × 62·5

Acquired by 1872

**P364 SHEEP**

Signed: *Rosa-Bonheur 57*

Canvas 46·4 × 65·1

Acquired by 1872

P364

**P365 A SHEPHERD'S DOG**

Signed: R. B. 64, and inscribed:BRIZO

Canvas 46·4 × 38·1

P365

**P372 ROE-DEER**

Signed: *Rosa-Bonheur*

Panel 19·1 × 24·8

Acquired by 1872

P372

# Richard Parkes BONINGTON
## 1802–1828

b. Arnold, near Nottingham, d. London; emigrated to Calais in 1817; pupil of Francia, the École des Beaux-Arts, and Gros, q.v.; friend of Delacroix, painter of historical genre and landscape.

**P270 A CHILD AT PRAYER**

Millboard 36·2 × 27·9

The lady is dressed in the costume of the 1630s and she appears to be wearing a widow's hood.

Purchased by the 4th Marquess of Hertford 1859(?)

P270

P273

### P273　A SEA PIECE

Canvas 54·6 × 84·5

Cleaned and restored 1978. Two water-colours by Bonington of the same composition are in private collections.

Acquired by 1872

P319

### P319　BERGUES, NEAR DUNKIRK

Panel 34·9 × 24·8

The topography may be somewhat fanciful; some of the details agree with those shown in a Bonington drawing of St. Omer. Bonington stayed at Dunkirk in 1824.

Acquired by 1872

P322

### P322　FRANÇOIS I AND MARGUERITE DE NAVARRE

Canvas 46·0 × 34·3

François I (1494–1547), whose likeness is founded on the portrait by Titian in the Louvre, inscribes on the window *Souvent femme varie, Bien fol qui s'y fie* (a verse attributed to him). Marguerite de Navarre (1492–1549), his sister, was also famed as a writer.

Purchased by the 4th Marquess of Hertford 1869

## P323    HENRI III AND THE ENGLISH AMBASSADOR

Canvas 54·9 × 66·0

Henri III (1551–89); in April 1571, when Duc d'Anjou, his hand was offered to Elizabeth I of England but the courtship, devised by his brother Charles IX, lasted only until July; Francis Walsingham was then the English Ambassador in Paris. It seems probable that this episode provided the subject of P323.

Purchased by the 4th Marquess of Hertford 1860

P323

## P333    ANNE PAGE AND SLENDER

Canvas 47·6 × 39·1

The characters taken from Shakespeare's *The Merry Wives of Windsor*.

Purchased by the 4th Marquess of Hertford 1853

P333

## P339    THE SEINE NEAR MANTES

Canvas 31·1 × 46·0

A preparatory sketch in sepia was sold at Sotheby's in 1949.

Acquired by 1872

P339

## P341    ON THE COAST OF PICARDY

Canvas 36·5 × 50·8

A lithograph by J. D. Harding, published in 1829, provides the title. A pencil sketch for part of the foreground is in the British Museum.

Purchased by the 4th Marquess of Hertford 1853

P341

P351

## P351  HENRI IV AND THE SPANISH AMBASSADOR

Canvas 39·3 × 53·0

The subject apparently derives from a canvas by Révoil exhibited at the Salon in 1817 (and also the source for the Ingres painting of the same title). The likenesses are based on older portraits: Henri IV from Pourbus; his Queen, Marie de Médicis, from Rubens; the Ambassador, Don Pedro, from Van der Venne. Exhibited in the Salon in 1827. See also P733 below, and Rubens, P522–24.

Purchased by the 4th Marquess of Hertford 1870

P362

## P362  LANDSCAPE WITH TIMBER WAGGON, FRANCE

Canvas 50·8 × 68·6

Several close variants are recorded, including a lithograph by Charles Lewis, entitled *The Waggon*.

Purchased by the 4th Marquess of Hertford 1852(?)

P375

## P375  THE PIAZZA SAN MARCO, VENICE

Canvas 100·3 × 81·6

Probably painted in 1827, but left unfinished. A more complete water colour of *c.* 1826 is in the Fitzwilliam Museum, Cambridge.

Acquired by 1872

### P656   THE DOGE'S PALACE, VENICE

Water-colour 20·0 × 27·3

Probably painted in 1826. A pencil study is in a private collection, and a larger oil version is in the Louvre.

Purchased by the 4th Marquess of Hertford 1843

P656

### P657   THE ARABIAN NIGHTS

Signed: *R.P. Bonington 1825*

Water-colour 24·1 × 18·7

The King, Scheherazade and her sister, the narrator and audience of *The Arabian Nights*.

Acquired by 1874

P657

### P668   MEDITATION

Water-colour 21·0 × 16·5

Signed: *R P Bonington 1826*

A mezzotint by S. W. Reynolds, published in 1827, provides the title. The figure of the young lady is derived from ter Borch's *Concert* in the Louvre, and that of the old woman from an engraving of Van Dyck's *Frances Bridges*.

Acquired by 1874

P668

### P672   THE ANTIQUARY

Water-colour 21·0 × 16·5

A mezzotint by S. W. Reynolds, and a lithograph by J. D. Harding, both of 1829, provide the title. A version in oils is in a private collection.

Purchased by the 4th Marquess of Hertford 1863

P672

P674

## P674   A VENETIAN SCENE

Signed: *RPB* (indistinct)

Water-colour 18·1 × 25·1

Purchased by the 4th Marquess of Hertford 1860

P675

## P675   THE EARL OF SURREY AND FAIR GERALDINE

Signed: *RPB*

Water-colour 14·0 × 10·8

Henry Howard, Earl of Surrey (1518–47), whose likeness is derived from the portrait of *A Young Man in red* at Hampton Court (formerly known as the *Earl of Surrey* by Holbein), had addressed a sonnet to 'Fair Geraldine' in 1537, when she was ten.

Acquired by 1872

P676

## P676   LADY AND PAGE

Water-colour 15·2 × 10·2

Probably painted in 1824, in which case this is one of the earliest of Bonington's costume pieces.

Purchased by the 4th Marquess of Hertford 1860

P678

## P678   THE LETTER

Signed: *RPB 1827*

Water-colour 15·2 × 10·2

Purchased by the 4th Marquess of Hertford 1860

### P679    LADY DRESSING HER HAIR

Signed: *RPB 1827*

Water-colour 15·2 × 10·2

Purchased by the 4th Marquess of Hertford 1860

P679

### P684    THE PIAZZETTA, VENICE

Water-colour 17·8 × 22·5

Probably painted in 1826. A variant water colour is in Manchester City Art Gallery, and a copy in the Laing Art Gallery, Newcastle. Two pencil drawings, related to P684, are in a private collection.

Acquired by 1874

P684

### P688    SOUVENIR OF VAN DYCK

Signed: *R. P. Bonington*

Water-colour 19·4 × 13.0

The figures are taken from Van Dyck's *Count of Nassau and his Family* (Firle), which was engraved by B. Baron in 1761.

Purchased by the 4th Marquess of Hertford 1864

P688

### P696    THE GREAT STAIRCASE OF A FRENCH CHÂTEAU

Signed: *R P Bonington 182[5 or 8]*

Water-colour 18·1 × 16·8

The dogs derive from Rubens's *Apotheosis of Henri IV* in the Louvre.

Acquired by 1874

P696

P698

## P698    OLD MAN AND CHILD

Signed: *R P Bonington 1827*

Water-colour 19·7 × 14·6

The man's features derive from a sketch by Tintoretto of the Doge Nicolo da Ponte (private collection).

Purchased by the 4th Marquess of Hertford 1863

P700

## P700    FISHING BOATS

Signed: *R P Bonington*

Water-colour 16·8 × 26·7

Title given on old mount as *A Dead Calm*.

Purchased by the 4th Marquess of Hertford 1843

P701

## P701    THE LEANING TOWERS, BOLOGNA

Water-colour 23·5 × 17·1

Bonington was at Bologna in 1826; the view is from the north side of the Palazzo del Podestà with the Torre Garisenda on the left and the Torre Asinelli on the right.

Purchased by the 4th Marquess of Hertford 1863

P704

## P704    ROUEN

Water-colour 18·1 × 23·8

Probably painted before 1822 when the central spire of the cathedral, seen here in the distance, collapsed.

Acquired by 1874

### P708   SUNSET IN THE PAYS DE CAUX

Signed: *R P B 1828*

Water-colour 19·7 × 26·4

Pays de Caux is the coastal district of Seine-Maritime, between Le Havre and Dieppe. Despite this traditional title, an engraving of 1836 (by W. Miller in *The Keepsake*) was lettered *Sea Shore, Cornwall*.

P708

Acquired by 1874

### P714   THE CHURCH OF SANT'AMBROGIO, MILAN

Signed: *RPB 1827*

Water-colour 21·9 × 28·6

Bonington passed through Milan in 1826. Two further versions exist in private collections.

P714

Purchased by the 4th Marquess of Hertford 1863

### P726   LA SIESTA

Signed: *RPB 182(8 or 6)*

Water-colour 19·1 × 13·3

Title on old mount given as *Scene in Venice*; a close variant was lithographed by J. D. Harding in 1829 as *Le Repos*. Also called *A Balcony Scene*.

Acquired by 1874

P726

### P727   CHARLES V VISITING FRANÇOIS I AFTER PAVIA

Water-colour 13·6 × 16·8

After his defeat by Imperial troops at Pavia in 1525 François I was confined in Madrid where he contracted a fever; the Emperor Charles V hurried to visit him, fearing for his life. A lithograph by J. D. Harding of 1829 confirms the title. Formerly in the collection of Clarkson Stanfield, q.v.

P727

Purchased by the 4th Marquess of Hertford 1843

P732

**P732    A LADY AND A CAVALIER**

Water-colour 14·0 × 10·5

Acquired by 1874

P733

**P733    HENRI IV AND THE SPANISH AMBASSADOR**

Water-colour 15·9 × 17·5

The same subject is represented in the oil by Bonington, P351, q.v., and the figures here derive from the same sources.

Purchased by the 4th Marquess of Hertford 1845(?)

P734

**P734    AN ODALISQUE**

Signed: *RPB 1827*

Water-colour 21·6 × 15·2

Purchased by the 4th Marquess of Hertford 1846

P749

**P749    MEDORA**

Signed: *R. P. Bonington 1826*

Water-colour 15·9 × 17·8

The subject is taken from Byron's *The Corsair* 1814 (see also H. Vernet, P368).

Acquired by 1874

**P750    TURK REPOSING**

Signed: *RPB 1826*

Water-colour 11·4 × 17·8

A related composition in oil by Bonington is called *The Chibouk* (National Gallery of Ireland, no. 537).

Purchased by the 4th Marquess of Hertford 1843

P750

# Francesco BONSIGNORI, attributed to
## 1455?–1519?

b. Verona, d. Caldiero; influenced by Mantegna and Cossa.

**P539    AN ITALIAN GENTLEMAN**

Panel 40·3 × 26·7

P539

# Gerard ter BORCH
## 1617–1681

b. Zwolle, d. Deventer; pupil of his father and P. de Molijn at Haarlem; travelled in Europe before 1654 when he settled in Deventer; portrait and genre painter.

**P235    A LADY DRESSING HER HAIR**

Signed: G.T.B.

Panel 36·2 × 27·9

Probably painted in the late 1650s. (HdG 48)

Purchased by Sir Richard Wallace 1872

P235

P236

**P236   A LADY READING A LETTER**

Canvas 45·1 × 33·3

Probably painted in the early 1660s; the model may be the artist's wife. (HdG 172)

Purchased by the 4th Marquess of Hertford 1848

# Jan BOTH
### *c.* 1618–1652

b. and d. Utrecht; pupil of Bloemart; travelled in Italy 1638–41; worked in Utrecht, a painter of Italianate landscapes. (James D. Burke, *Jan Both*, New York, 1976)

P28

**P28   ITALIAN LANDSCAPE**

Signed: *JBoth*

Canvas 79·7 × 105·4

Dated *c.* 1645 by Burke. (HdG 123, Burke 56)

Acquired by 1872

P198

**P198   ITALIAN COAST SCENE**

Signed: *JBoth fe.*

Panel 47·6 × 66·7

Dated mid-1640s by Burke. (HdG 111, Burke 57)

Acquired by 1872

## Ascribed to BOTH

**P24    LANDSCAPE WITH A DRINKING POOL**

Canvas 85·4 × 111·4

Purchased as a work by Pynacker, the attribution to Both remains open to question. (HdG 122 as Pynacker)

Purchased by the 4th Marquess of Hertford 1858

P24

# François BOUCHER

## 1703–1770

b. and d. Paris; pupil of Lemoyne, q.v.; travelled in Italy with Carle van Loo, q.v., returning to Paris 1731; worked under Oudry, q.v., for the tapestry manufactories of Beauvais and the Gobelins, succeeding him as *Inspecteur* at the Gobelins 1755; much patronised by Mme. de Pompadour (see P418); *premier peintre du roi* and director of the Académie 1765. (A. Ananoff, *Boucher*, 2 vols., Paris, 1976)

**P385    SHEPHERD WATCHING A SLEEPING SHEPHERDESS**

Signed: *f. Boucher 174[5?]*

Canvas 109·9 × 155·6

The sleeping shepherdess was engraved by Bonnet as *La dormeuse*. (Ananoff 292)

Purchased by the 4th Marquess of Hertford 1865(?)

P385

P390

### P390 THE MODISTE

Signed: *f. Boucher*

Canvas 63·8 × 53·0

A replica of a painting in the Nationalmuseum, Stockholm, which is signed and dated 1746. Also known as *Le matin*, one of a set of four compositions illustrating the times of day. Engraved by R. Gaillard as *La marchande des modes*. (Ananoff 297/4)

Acquired by 1872

P399

### P399 SHEPHERD PIPING TO A SHEPHERDESS

Canvas 95·2 × 143·5

Originally a shaped canvas with rounded bottom corners and scalloped top corners. Probably painted in 1745. (Ananoff 283)

Acquired by 1872

P411

### P411 VENUS AND CUPID WITH DOVES

Signed: *Boucher 1754*

Canvas 83·2 × 140·3

Engraved by Bonnet as *Vénus caressée par l'Amour*. Pendant to P423. (Ananoff 433)

P418

### P418 THE MARQUISE DE POMPADOUR

Signed: *f. Boucher 1759*

Canvas 91·1 × 68·9

Jeanne-Antoine Poisson (1721–64), as Louis XV's mistress cr. Marquise de Pompadour 1745; she exerted considerable influence on Court patronage of the arts, particularly towards Boucher and the Sèvres porcelain factory. P418 was commissioned by the sitter, as was the marble group which appears in the background (Pigalle's *L'amour et l'amitié* of 1758). (Ananoff 522)

Purchased by the 4th Marquess of Hertford 1869(?)

### P423    VENUS WITH TWO PUTTI

Signed: *Boucher 1754*

Canvas 83·2 × 140·3

Pendant to P411. (Ananoff 434)

P423

### P429    THE VISIT OF VENUS TO VULCAN

Signed: *f. Boucher 1754*

Canvas 166·1 × 85·4

Venus, Goddess of Love, wife of Vulcan, God of Fire. One of a set of four canvases (see P432, P438 and P444) whose original location remains unknown; they were sold in 1851 as a folding screen with a Lancret composition on the back of each. (Ananoff 428)

Purchased by the 4th Marquess of Hertford 1851

P429

### P431    SHEPHERD AND SHEPHERDESS REPOSING

Signed: *f. Boucher 1761*

Canvas 77·5 × 64·8

Exhibited in the Salon of 1761. (Ananoff 543).

Acquired by 1872

P431

P432

## P432    CUPID A CAPTIVE

Signed: *f. Boucher*

Canvas 166·4 × 84·8

See P429 above. (Ananoff 429)

Purchased by the 4th Marquess of Hertford 1851

P438

## P438    VENUS AND MARS SURPRISED BY VULCAN

Canvas 166·4 × 85·4

See P429. Vulcan ensnares Venus with Mars, God of War (Ovid *Metamorphoses*, iv). (Ananoff 430)

Purchased by the 4th Marquess of Hertford 1851

## P444 THE JUDGMENT OF PARIS

Signed: *f. Boucher 1754*

Canvas 166·7 × 85·4

See P429. Paris awards the golden apple to Venus, at the expense of Juno and Minerva. (Ananoff 431)

Purchased by the 4th Marquess of Hertford 1851

P444

## P445 SPRING

Signed: *f. Boucher 1745*

Canvas 100·3 × 135·6

Engraved by Duflos as *La toilette pastorale*. With P447, *Le retour de chasse de Diane* (Musée Cognacq-Jay), and *Les confidences pastorales* (Los Angeles County Museum), P445 formed part of a set of overdoors originally installed in *Les Folies de Chartres*, the château of the duc de Chartres. Copies of the four are in the *salon de la pendule* at Versailles. (Ananoff 281)

Purchased by the 4th Marquess of Hertford 1857

P445

P446

## P446  JUPITER IN THE SHAPE OF DIANA SURPRISES CALLISTO

Signed: *f. Boucher 1769*

Canvas 160·0 × 130·2

The subject is taken from Ovid's *Metamorphoses*, ii. A late re-working of a subject previously exhibited at the Salons of 1761 and 1765; another version signed and dated 1769 is in a private collection. P446 was probably the original subject of the Gobelins tapestry executed in 1776–78 and given to the Grand Duke Paul of Russia in 1782. (Ananoff 668)

Purchased by Sir Richard Wallace 1872

P447

## P447  AUTUMN

Signed: *f. Boucher 1745*

Canvas 101·3 × 134·6

See P445. Engraved by Duflos as *Erigone vaincue* (with verses suggesting that here Bacchus, God of Wine, ravishes Erigone by changing himself into a nymph). (Ananoff 282)

Purchased by the 4th Marquess of Hertford 1857

P481

## P481  NYMPH AND CUPID WITH MUSICAL EMBLEMS

Canvas 101·6 × 147·3

Dated 1752 by Ananoff. (Ananoff 390)

Acquired by 1888

## P482    AN AUTUMN PASTORAL

Signed: *f. Boucher 1749*

Canvas 263·5 × 201·3

Pendant to P489; they originally decorated the *grand salon* on the ground floor of the château at Montigny-Lencoup, very probably commissioned by the *intendant des finances* Trudaine (who built the château and commissioned the four Oudrys, P625, P627, P629 and P631, q.v.). The subject is reproduced in reverse on a Sèvres vase in The Wallace Collection. (Ananoff 336 as *Pensent-ils aux raisins*)

P482

## P484   THE RAPE OF EUROPA

Canvas 233·7 × 276·2

Europa abducted by Jupiter in the form of a bull (Ovid, *Metamorphoses*, ii). Pendant to P487. Dated 1734 by Ananoff, but probably later; influenced by Lemoyne to whom both pictures were once attributed. (Ananoff 104)

Purchased by the 4th Marquess of Hertford 1843

P484

## P485  THE RISING OF THE SUN

Signed: *f. Boucher 1753*

Canvas 321·3 × 270·5

Apollo, God of the Sun, prepares to embark in
his horse-drawn chariot, at break of day. With
P486 a design for a Gobelins tapestry, acquired
by the Marquise de Pompadour from the
Manufactory. They show Boucher at his most
confident and effective. A fine drawing for the
figure of Apollo appeared in the Daniels sale
1978; for another of the triton see Appendix
PA1. (Ananoff 422)

Purchased by the 4th Marquess of Hertford
1855

P485

## P486   THE SETTING OF THE SUN

Signed: *f. Boucher 1753*

Canvas 323·8 × 264·2

See P485. At the end of the day Apollo leaves his chariot and comes to the arms of the waiting Thetys. (Ananoff 423)

Purchased by the 4th Marquess of Hertford 1855

P486

### P487   MERCURY CONFIDING THE INFANT BACCHUS TO THE NYMPHS

Canvas 233·7 × 276·2

As messenger of the Gods, Mercury entrusts the threatened Bacchus, son of Jupiter, to the nymphs of Nysa. Pendant to P484, q.v. Dated 1734 by Ananoff but probably later. (Ananoff 106)

Purchased by the 4th Marquess of Hertford 1843

P487

### P489    A SUMMER PASTORAL

Signed: *f. Boucher 1749*

Canvas 262·9 × 201·3

Pendant to P482, q.v.. Engraved by R. Gaillard as *Le berger recompensé*. (Ananoff 337)

P489

P490

### P490    THE MUSE POLYHYMNIA (?)

Canvas 101·6 × 147·3

Apparently the picture engraved by Daullé in 1756 as *la Muse Clio* belonging to the Marquise de Pompadour, but in her sale, 1766, described as *Polymnie* (the muse of the sublime hymn). The attributes seem more those of Euterpe (muse of lyric poetry). A pendant, formerly in the collection of Sir Richard Wallace, *Terpsichore* (muse of dance and song) was last sold in 1951. (Ananoff 487)

## Studio of BOUCHER

**P433  THE TRIUMPH OF
AMPHITRITE**

Canvas 69·2 × 120·7

An extended version of *The Birth of Venus* (New
York, private collection), probably executed
in Boucher's studio (Ananoff 243/14)

Acquired by 1872

P433

## After BOUCHER

**P467  LA TOILETTE DE VÉNUS**

Water-colour 13·3 × 10·8

From the painting of this title now in a private
collection, New York, dated 1743 (Ananoff
245).

P467

**P468  THE TRIUMPH OF
AMPHITRITE**

Water-colour 13·3 × 10·8

From the painting *Naissance et triomphe de Vénus*,
now unlocated (Ananoff 244).

P468

## Follower of BOUCHER

**P766  DANAE AND THE GOLDEN RAIN**

Canvas on panel 19·7 × 22·2

The subject is taken from Ovid, *Metamorphoses*,
iv (see also Titian, After, P546). A miniature in
the Collection, M139, follows the same design
closely.

P766

P776

### P776   AMORINI

Red chalk 17·8 × 16·2

Not derived from a known Boucher design, and only connected with the master in the loosest way.

## Esaias BOURSSE
### 1631–1672

b. Amsterdam, d. at sea; visited Italy, worked in Amsterdam from *c.* 1653.

P166

### P166   INTERIOR: WOMAN COOKING

Signed: *L. Boursse 1656*

Canvas 51·8 × 58·4

Though the signature now appears to read *L. Boursse*, and a hypothetical L. Boursse has been proposed as an independent personality (e.g. in Bénézit's *Dictonary*), P166 is consistent with the work of Esaias, and the initial is probably rubbed.

Purchased by Sir Richard Wallace 1872

## Jacques-Raymond BRASCASSAT
### 1804–1867

b. Bordeaux, d. Paris; studied at the École des Beaux-Arts, Paris; painted landscapes and animal subjects.

P363

### P363   GOAT AND KID

Signed: *Dal Vero – R. Brascassat*

Canvas 38·4 × 46·4

Acquired by 1872

P721

### P721   DOGS ATTACKING A WOLF

Signed: *J.R. Brascassat 1838*

Water-colour 42·6 × 55·6

Purchased by the 4th Marquess of Hertford 1863(?)

# BRONZINO, after
1503–1572

b. Monticelli, near Florence, d. Florence; pupil of Pontormo and Raffaellino del Garbo; worked in Florence.

### P555  ELEONORA DI TOLEDO, GRAND DUCHESS OF TUSCANY

Inscribed: FALLAX GRATIA ET VANA EST PULCHRITUDO ('Charm is a delusion and beauty fleeting', *Proverbs* xxxi, 30)

Panel 79·4 × 60·3

Daughter of Pedro di Toledo, Eleonora (d. 1562) m. Cosimo dei Medici in 1539; he became Grand Duke of Tuscany in 1559. P555, a reduced version of the three-quarter length in the Uffizi, was probably a posthumous tribute; the empty urn and the inscription (used in the mass for a holy woman) encourage such an interpretation.

P555

Acquired by 1872

# ADRIAEN BROUWER
1606?–1638

b. Oudenarde, d. Antwerp; pupil of Frans Hals, q.v.; worked in Amsterdam, Haarlem and Antwerp.

### P211  A BOOR ASLEEP

Panel 36·8 × 27·6

A signed version is in the Badische Kunsthalle, Karlsruhe. (HdG64)

Acquired by 1857

P211

# Alexandre CALAME
## 1810–1864

b. Vevey, Switzerland, d. Mentone; pupil of Diday

P588

**P588   A WATERFALL NEAR ROSENLAUI IN SWITZERLAND**

Signed: *A. Calame*

Canvas 83·5 × 67·3

Inscribed, verso, by the artist: *Souvenir des environs de Rosenlaui, Canton de Berne, peint pour Mr Durand Ruel. Terminé en juin 1860. Toile 81 cent. de haut., 65 c. de large. Génève, 26 juin 1860. A. Calame.* The figures are said to be by François Bonheur (1824–84), younger brother of Rosa Bonheur, q.v.

Purchased by the 4th Marquess of Hertford 1865

# William CALLOW
## 1812–1908

b. Greenwich, d. Great Missenden, Bucks.; studied in Paris, professor of water-colour painting to the family of King Louis-Philippe.

P746

**P746   ENTERING THE HARBOUR**

Signed: *W. Callow 1842*

Water-colour 23·5 × 31·2

Formerly called *French fishing boats.*

Acquired by 1872

# Abraham van CALRAERT
## 1642–1722

b. and d. Dordrecht; much influenced by Cuyp, q.v. with whom his work has been sometimes confused, both stylistically and because of his A.C. signature.

**P172   TWO HORSEMEN AT A TAVERN BY A RIVER**

Inscribed: *A. Cuyp*

Panel 39·7 × 55·6

A composition derived from two paintings by Cuyp, P51 in this collection, and another in a private collection, U.S.A. Another version, signed *A.C.*, was in an English private collection in 1947. (HdG 512, ?530, as Cuyp).

Purchased by the 4th Marquess of Hertford 1851

P172

### P180 CATTLE ON A RIVER BANK

Signed: *A.C.*

Panel 34·3 × 53·3

(HdG 207, 246, 247 as Cuyp)

Purchased by the 4th Marquess of Hertford 1856(?)

P180

### P228 HALT AT AN INN

Inscribed: *A. Cuyp*

Panel 38·7 × 58·7

The bay horse stands identically with that in a picture signed *A. C.* in the Fitzwilliam Museum, Cambridge (no. 36). (HdG 513, 526, as Cuyp).

Purchased by the 4th Marquess of Hertford 1848

P228

## Govert CAMPHUIJSEN
### 1623/4–1672

b. Gorkum, buried Amsterdam; influenced by Paul Potter, q.v.; worked in Amsterdam, and in Stockholm between 1652 and 1663.

### P132 A DUTCH FARM AT SUNSET

Signed: *G. Camphuijsen*

Panel 84·5 × 115·3

Purchased by the 4th Marquess of Hertford 1859

P132

# CANALETTO (Giovanni Antonio Canal)
## 1697–1768

b. and d. Venice; studied under his father, Bernardo, as a scene-painter; earliest Venetian views date from 1723; visited England between 1746 and *c.* 1755; pressure of commissioned works (particularly from English patrons) led to an involved studio practice. See also Venetian School P498, P513; Italian School P493. (W. G. Constable, *Canaletto*, 2 vols., 1962, revised by J. G. Links, 1976).

P496

### P496   A REGATTA ON THE GRAND CANAL

Canvas 59·7 × 94·0

A race on the Grand Canal for which prizes would be given from the temporary *macchina* (left foreground); the Palazzo Balbi is immediately beyond it. A mechanical work by Canaletto; the earliest version of this subject, executed *c.* 1730, is at Windsor. (Constable 352, as attributed)

Acquired by the 4th Marquess of Hertford by 1859

### P497   THE BACINO DI SAN MARCO FROM SAN GIORGIO MAGGIORE

Canvas 130·5 × 189·9

View taken from the campanile of San Giorgio, showing Santa Maria della Salute (centre left) and the Ducal Palace (right) across the water. Probably painted 1735–40, as a pendant to P499, though on a different weave of canvas. (Constable 137)

Acquired by the 3rd Marquess of Hertford

P497

### P499 THE BACINO DI SAN MARCO LOOKING EAST FROM THE GIUDECCA

Canvas 130·8 × 189·9

The Dogana (extreme left) and San Giorgio Maggiore (right distance). Painted after 1726–28, possibly pendant to P497. Evidently assembled from separate preliminary drawings; the Dogana is slightly out of perspective with the rest of the composition. (Constable 134)

Acquired by the 3rd Marquess of Hertford

P499

### P507 VIEW ON THE CANALE DI SANTA CHIARA LOOKING SOUTH-EAST

Canvas 59·7 × 94·0

The (now demolished) Church of Santa Croce faces the wall of the convent of Corpus Christi at the farthest point. Pendant to P511. (Constable 268, as by Canaletto, but of mechanical, replica quality)

Acquired by the 4th Marquess of Hertford by 1859

P507

### P509 THE DOGE'S PALACE AND THE RIVA DEGLI SCHIAVONI LOOKING EAST

Canvas 60·3 × 95·2

Pendant to P516. (Constable 112)

Acquired by 1872

P509

P511

## P511  THE GRAND CANAL: THE RIALTO BRIDGE FROM THE SOUTH

Canvas 59·7 × 94·0

The Palazzo Manin (extreme right). Pendant to P507.

A mechanical version of a painting last recorded on the Paris art market in 1930. (Constable 228.2)

Acquired by the 3rd Marquess of Hertford

P514

*after  Canaletto*

## P514  THE PIAZZETTA AND THE DOGE'S PALACE FROM THE BACINO DI SAN MARCO

Canvas 52·7 × 70·2

A version of the painting in the Brera, Milan. (Constable 107a, as studio repetition, probably in part by Canaletto)

Purchased by the 4th Marquess of Hertford 1855

P516

## P516  SANTA MARIA DELLA SALUTE FROM THE PIAZZETTA

Canvas 60·3 × 95·2

Church of the Redentore on the Giudecca (extreme left). Pendant to P509. (Constable 90)

Acquired by 1872

## *after* CANALETTO and ~~studio assistants~~

P492

## P492  THE GRAND CANAL LOOKING SOUTH

Canvas 48·6 × 79·7

The Palazzo Moro-Lin (left foreground). A studio version of the larger picture at Windsor, and see P510 below. Forms a group with P495, P512 and P515 (see Imitators of Canaletto). (Constable 203a, as school of Canaletto).

Acquired by the 4th Marquess of Hertford by 1859

*studio of Canaletto*

**P500 A FESTIVAL IN THE PIAZZETTA**

Canvas 59.7 × 93.7

The Maundy Thursday celebration with an acrobatic performance (*Le Forze di Ercole*); the ropes shown (attached to the Campanile) allowed a small boy to 'fly' to the Doge's box where he recited verses. One of twelve *Solennità Dogali* originally engraved by G. B. Brustolon after drawings by Canaletto (see also Venetian School P513). (Constable 330 vii 1)

Acquired by the 3rd Marquess of Hertford

P500

*Studio of Canaletto*

**P505 THE PIAZZA SAN MARCO LOOKING WEST**

Canvas 59.1 × 127.0

The triple arcade of the Campanile's loggia (extreme left) has been fancifully reduced to a single arch. Catalogued in 1968 as largely by studio assistants, but accepted by Constable as by Canaletto himself. (Constable 30)

Acquired by 1872

P505

*Canaletto*

**P506 THE GRAND CANAL LOOKING EAST**

Canvas 47.0 × 77.5

The Palazzo Flangini (extreme left). Pendant to P510. Catalogued in 1968 as predominantly by studio assistants, but accepted by Constable as by Canaletto himself. (Constable 257)

Acquired by 1872(?)

P506

*Canaletto*

**P510 THE GRAND CANAL LOOKING SOUTH TO SANTA MARIA DELLA CARITA**

Canvas 46.4 × 77.5

See P492 above. Pendant to P506. Catalogued in 1968 as predominantly by studio assistants, but accepted by Constable as by Canaletto himself. (Constable 205)

Acquired by 1872(?)

P510

## Imitators of CANALETTO

### P495   SANTA MARIA DELLA SALUTE

P495

Canvas 48·6 × 79·7

Entrance to the Grand Canal looking east. Forms a group with P492, P512 and P515 below. From the painting at Windsor. (Constable 170 c 1, as school of Canaletto)

Acquired by the 4th Marquess of Hertford by 1859

### P501   OLD NORTHUMBERLAND HOUSE, CHARING CROSS

P501

Canvas 72·7 × 113·0

The house was demolished in 1874. From the painting by Canaletto executed in 1752 for the 1st Duke of Northumberland. Other close variants have recently been sold as by William James and Joseph Paul. (Constable 419b, as school of Canaletto)

Purchased by Sir Richard Wallace 1873

### P512   THE GRAND CANAL LOOKING EAST WITH THE PALAZZO CORNER DELLA CA'GRANDE

P512

Canvas 48·6 × 79·7

Forms a group with P492, P495 and P515. From the painting at Windsor, painted before 1730. (Constable 184a, as school of Canaletto)

### P515   THE SALUTE AND THE DOGANA FROM THE MOLO

P515

Canvas 48·6 × 79·7

The Fonteghetto della Farina (extreme right). Forms a group with P492, P495 and P512. From the painting in the National Gallery, Washington. (Constable 153a, as studio of Canaletto)

## Alonso CANO
### 1601–1667

b. and d. Granada: painter, sculptor and architect; pupil of Velazquez, q.v., Pacheco and Juan del Castillo; worked in Seville, Madrid and Granada.

**P15  THE VISION OF SAINT JOHN THE EVANGELIST**

Canvas 83·8 × 45·1

The subject is taken from *Revelation* xxi, 9–14. From a polyptych of eight scenes from the life of St John the Evangelist painted for the nuns of Santa Paula, Seville, between 1635 and 1638; P15 was the lower right-hand panel. Two further scenes (each 71 × 38) are in the Ringling Museum, Sarasota.

Purchased by the 4th Marquess of Hertford 1852

P15

# Philippe de CHAMPAIGNE
## 1602–1674

b. Brussels, d. Paris; came to Paris 1621, worked with Duchesne and the young Poussin, q.v., at the Luxembourg Palace before 1624; patronised by Marie de Médicis, Richelieu and Louis XIII (*peintre du roi* 1637); latterly withdrew into the Jansenist circle at Port-Royal. (B. Dorival, *Philippe de Champaigne*, 2 vols., Paris, 1976)

**P119  MARRIAGE OF THE VIRGIN**

Signed: P. CHAMPAIGNE, F

Panel 74·3 × 142·9

The Priest joins the hands of Joseph and Mary who is attended by maidens; her rejected suitors stand to the right. The little girl (extreme right) is thought to be the artist's daughter, Catherine, who was 10 in 1647. Painted *c.* 1644–46 for the oratory of Anne of Austria at the Palais Royal. (Dorival 19)

Purchased by the 4th Marquess of Hertford 1865

P119

P127

## P127    AN ÉCHEVIN OF PARIS

Canvas 72·7 × 59·7

One of the biennially-elected municipal coun-
cillors of Paris (although identified by Dorival
as Martin Lemaire, *greffier* 1634–60). A fragment from one of two lost group portraits by
Champaigne painted for the Hôtel de Ville,
Paris, in 1652 and 1656; the shoulder of a
second figure is discernible, bottom left.
(Dorival 174, as a separate copy from a group
portrait)

Acquired by 1872

## P129    THE ADORATION OF THE
SHEPHERDS

Canvas 233·0 × 163·2

Commissioned by Cardinal Richelieu and
presented by him to the abbaye de Quincey,
near Poitiers, in 1628. An early work reflecting
Flemish    influence,    particularly    Rubens.
(Dorival 35)

Purchased by the 4th Marquess of Hertford
1849

P129

## P134    THE ANNUNCIATION

Canvas 336·6 × 215·9

From the mid-1640s, probably first placed in the church of Culture-Sainte-Catherine in Paris; it has also been supposed that, with P119 above, it may have been painted for the Palais Royal. An oil sketch for P134 is in the Ferens Art Gallery, Hull. (Dorival 24, as from the Palais Royal painted in 1644)

Purchased by the 4th Marquess of Hertford 1845

P134

## After de CHAMPAIGNE

### P645   JEAN DU VERGER DE HAURANNE, ABBE DE ST. CYRAN

P645

Inscribed: *Mre IEAN DV VERGER DE HAVRANNE | ABBÉ de St. Cyran decedé l'11 d'Oct$^{re}$ 1643 agé de | 62 ans*

Panel 16·5 × 11·4

The Abbé de St. Cyran (1581–1643) was an influential and rigorous Jansenist at Port-Royal, imprisoned by Richelieu 1638–43. He refused ever to have his portrait taken, and Champaigne's posthumous image derives from a death mask. P645 is one of many versions of the three-quarter length at Versailles, painted *c.* 1664–68. (Dorival 1791)

## Jacques CHARLIER

### 1720–1790

Miniaturist, possibly a pupil of Boucher whose works he copied; patronised by the Court, the comte de Caylus and the prince de Conti; see also *Catalogue of Miniatures*.

### P474   CUPID OFFERING AN APPLE TO VENUS

P474

Gouache on vellum 23·5 × 17·5

A reduced version of a lost painting by Boucher of 1743 (Ananoff 269), formerly in the collection of the prince de Conti (who commissioned a copy from Charlier, now in a private collection in Paris).

### P475   THE BIRTH OF VENUS

Gouache on vellum 69·8 × 50·8

A reduced copy of the painting by Boucher in the Detroit Institute of Art (painted in 1765, Ananoff 619), the composition here extended to the right and reduced in height.

P475

**P476  THE JUDGEMENT OF PARIS**

Gouache on vellum 23·5 × 17·5

For the subject, see Boucher P444. A reduced version of a painting by Boucher of 1759 in a private collection, Paris (Ananoff 524). The prince de Conti owned an earlier version of this subject by Boucher (Ananoff 270) which he had copied by Charlier, cf. P474 above.

P476

# Giovanni Battista CIMA da Conegliano
## 1459/60?–1517/18

b. Conegliano, north of Venice; active in Venice 1492–1516.

**P1  SAINT CATHERINE OF ALEXANDRIA**

Signed: JOANIS BABTISTE CONEG-LANESIS OPUS

Panel 153·4 × 77·5

The Saint's attributes include the palm of martyrdom and the broken wheel, a relic of her torture. The central panel from a polyptych, dateable *c.* 1500, from the church of San Rocco, Mestre, near Venice; two wings (showing SS. Sebastian and Roch) are in the Musée des Beaux-Arts, Strasbourg. An engraving of the complete polyptych by A. Baratti (1724–87) shows that P1 has been reduced (perhaps by 25 cm) there having been an architrave above joining the pillars. The lunette panel (40 × 71) exhibited with P1 was presented to The Wallace Collection by Mr and Mrs George Blumenthal in 1933.

Purchased by the 4th Marquess of Hertford 1859

P1

# CLAUDE (Claude Gellée, called Le Lorrain)
## 1600–1682

b. Chamagne (Lorraine) d. Rome; in Rome by *c.* 1613; studied with Tassi; from 1627 worked in Rome, the outstanding exponent of the classical landscape.

P114

### P114   MERCURY STEALING THE HERDS OF ADMETUS FROM APOLLO

Signed: CLAUDE IV / ROMA / 1660

Canvas 75·6 × 111·4

Mercury (mid-distance), Apollo playing his pipe (left foreground); the subject is taken from Ovid, *Metamorphoses*, i and ii; a pendant to the *Landscape with Mercury and Battus* (Chatsworth). Cleaned and restored 1978, when it was confirmed that Apollo and his dog were later additions. The dog was first recorded in 1738.

Purchased by the 4th Marquess of Hertford 1846

## After CLAUDE

P125

### P125   COAST SCENE WITH CLASSICAL BUILDINGS

Canvas 43·2 × 55·2

An 18th- or possibly early-19th-century version of the *Harbour Scene* of 1638 now in a private collection.

Purchased by the 4th Marquess of Hertford 1857

## Joos van CLEVE, after
### active 1511 d. 1540/1

b. Antwerp; portrait painter active in the Courts of Italy, France and England.

P551

### P551   FRANÇOIS I

Panel 15·9 × 13·0

François I (1494–1547) ascended the French throne in 1515. One of several versions of a portrait by van Cleve, the best probably that in the Philadelphia Museum of Art. For two earlier images of François I, see *Catalogue of Sculpture*, S339 and S347; see also Bonington P322, P727.

# François CLOUET, after

### c. 1515–c. 1572

b. Tours, d. Paris; portrait painter and draughtsman, worked for the French Court.

## P530   QUEEN MARY STUART

Inscribed: MARIE. STUART. REYNE. D'ESCOSSE / VEVFE.DE.FRANCOIS. SECOND / ROY.DE.FRANCE.

Panel 39·1 × 30·2

An old label, verso, repeats the inscription. Mary Stuart (1542–87), daughter of James V of Scotland, mother of James I of England, m. 1559 François II of France (who d. 1560); executed 1587. This image dates from after 1560 as the sitter wears royal (white) mourning for her husband. Clouet's original drawing for this image is in the Bibliothèque Nationale but several other painted versions are known.

P530

Acquired by 1872

# Léon COGNIET

### 1794–1880

b. and d. Paris; pupil Guérin; painter of romantic and military subjects.

## P279   REBECCA AND SIR BRIAN DE BOIS GUILBERT

Signed: *Léon Cogniet 1828*

Canvas 90·2 × 116·5

The subject is taken from Scott's *Ivanhoe* 1820; exhibited in the Salon of 1831.

Acquired by 1872

P279

## P681   THE DEFENCE OF PARIS 1814

Signed: *Léon Cogniet*

Water-colour 24·1 × 18·4

Title given on old mount as *The Polish Standard-Bearer 1814*. The standard is inscribed *Mareng*[o?] . . . *Jena*[?] / *Français . . . Polonais* . . .

Acquired by 1872

P681

P685

**P685   THE RETREAT FROM MOSCOW 1812**

Signed: *Léon Cogniet*

Water-colour 24·8 × 18·7

A lithograph (recorded in a private collection) is lettered *Praga 1831 Dedié aux Polonais*.

Acquired by 1874

# Thomas Sidney COOPER
## 1803–1902

b. and d. Canterbury; studied with Verboekhoven, q.v., in Belgium 1827–31; worked in Canterbury, influenced by 17th-century Dutch animal painters. (S. Sartin, *T. S. Cooper*, Leigh-on-Sea, 1976)

P309

**P309   CATTLE**

Signed: *T. Sidney Cooper R.A. 1852* (the 'R.A.' a later addition)

Canvas 77·5 diameter

(Sartin 100)

Acquired by 1872

# Gonzales COQUES
## 1614/18–1684

b. and d. Antwerp; President of the Antwerp Guild of St Luke 1664; his royal patrons included Charles I of England.

## P92   A FAMILY GROUP IN A LANDSCAPE

Canvas 118·1 × 175·9

Dated *1647*. The Neptune fountain (far left) appears in several of Coques's compositions (e.g. P223 below). The young couple (far right) derive from a Rubens-Snijders composition (now on loan to the National Museum of Wales). The landscape has been attributed to Frans Wouters (1614–59).

Purchased by the 4th Marquess of Hertford 1857

P92

## P162   A GENTLEMAN WITH HIS TWO DAUGHTERS

Copper 48·3 × 61·0

The caryatids are adapted from Rubens's portrait of the Gerbier family (National Gallery, Washington). Formerly called *The Painter's Family*.

P162

## P223   FAMILY GROUP BY A FOUNTAIN

Panel 54·6 × 72·4

The Neptune fountain recurs in P92 above. Probably painted *c.* 1660.

Purchased by the 4th Marquess of Hertford 1859

P223

# CORNEILLE de Lyon, workshop of
## active 1533/4–1574

b. The Hague; naturalised as French 1547; *peintre du roi* under Henri II and Charles IX.

P532

### P532   EARL OF HERTFORD, called

Inscribed: M. LE COMTE DE HERTFORD

Panel 21·0 × 13·7

Two other versions of this image are each inscribed with different identities: *François I* (Louvre) and *François Gouffier* (French private collection). Edward Seymour (1506–52), cr. Earl of Hertford 1537, Duke of Somerset 1547, Lord Protector 1547, was the ancestor of the Marquesses of Hertford.

Acquired by 1872

# Jean-Baptiste-Camille COROT
## 1796–1875

b. and d. Paris; travelled in Italy 1825–28, 1835 and 1843; landscape painter, allied with the Barbizon school.

### P281   MACBETH AND THE WITCHES

Signed: *Corot* (twice)

Canvas 111·1 × 135·9

The subject is taken from Shakespeare's *Macbeth* iv, 1. Probably the picture exhibited in the Salon of 1867, *Macbeth; les sorcières*. Corot had previously shown a *Macbeth; paysage* in the 1859 Salon.

Acquired by 1872

P281

# Jacques COURTOIS, called Il Borgognone
## 1621–1676

b. Saint-Hippolyte, d. Rome; served as a soldier in Milan 1636–39; worked in Bologna, Florence and Rome as a battle painter and etcher.

### P769   THE DUKE OF PARMA DINES ON THE BATTLEFIELD

Sepia, pen and wash 15·2 × 20·6

Inscribed on the mount *Borgognone* and, *verso*, in Italian describing the subject, confirming that this is a preliminary study for the left hand group in Courtois' etching *The Capture of Oudenarde*, published in 1647 in vol. 2 of *De Bello Belgico* by Famianus Strada. The battle of Oudenarde was fought in 1587.

P769

# Thomas COUTURE
## 1815–1879

b. Senlis, d. Villiers-le-Bel; pupil of Gros, q.v., and Delaroche, q.v.; history and portrait painter, amongst his many pupils was Manet.

### P262   THE YOUNG DRUMMER

Signed: *T.C.*

Canvas 26·7 × 21·6

A reduced replica of a canvas on the New York art market in 1968 (147 × 114, dated 1857).

Acquired by 1872

P262

### P265   TIMON OF ATHENS

Signed: *T.C. 1857*

Canvas 19·1 × 24·1

The subject may be based on Shakespeare's *Timon of Athens*, iv, but it is possibly a re-working of Couture's *Amour de l'or* of 1844, the theme being greed rather than misanthropy.

Acquired by 1872

P265

P288

### P288   HARLEQUIN AND PIERROT

Signed: *T.C.*

Canvas 12·1 × 15·6

A scene from a fancy-dress ball, and probably connected with P370 below. A reduced replica of a canvas in the Chrysler Art Museum, Norfolk, Virginia (113 × 147, dated 1857).

Acquired by 1872

P340

### P340   A ROMAN FEAST

Signed: *T.C. 1843*

Canvas 38·1 × 46·4

One of the earliest sketches which may be connected with the celebrated *Les Romains de la décadence* of 1847 (Louvre, 466 × 775); this motif does not appear exactly in the final picture.

Acquired by 1872

P370

### P370   THE DUEL AFTER THE MASKED BALL

Signed: *T.C. '57*

Canvas 24·1 × 32·7

Pierrot (right) and Harlequin (left) prepare for a duel; possibly based on an actual duel fought in the winter of 1856–57 between Delun-Montaud and S-C-J. Boitelle after a masquerade. A painting by Gérôme, showing Pierrot struck by Harlequin, also dated 1857, is at Chantilly (another version in the Walters Art Gallery, Baltimore). See also P288 above.

Acquired by 1872

# Carlo CRIVELLI
## active 1457–1493

A native of Venice; in Zara (now Yugoslavia) 1465, thereafter working mainly in the Marches.

**P527   SAINT ROCH**

Panel 43·2 × 11·4

The Saint, invoked against the plague, displays a sore on his right thigh. Evidently part of a dismembered polyptych, P527 has been tentatively associated with the *St Sebastian* in the Museo Poldi-Pezzoli, Milan.

P527

# Aelbert CUYP
## 1620–1691

b. and d. Dordrecht; studied with his father J. G. Cuyp; worked in Dordrecht, influenced by Van Goyen and Jan Both, q.v.; landscape, animal and occasional portrait painter.

**P49   SHIPPING ON THE MAAS, DORDRECHT**

Signed: *A. Cuyp*

Canvas 102·2 × 153·0

Probably from the early 1650s, an unusual subject for Cuyp; a more dramatic adaptation is in the National Gallery, London, no. 6405. Cleaned and restored 1976. Related drawings are in the Kunsthalle, Hamburg (right hand side), and the British Museum (the foreground boat). (HdG 639).

Purchased by the 4th Marquess of Hertford 1857

P49

P51

**P51   THE AVENUE AT MEERDERVOORT, DORDRECHT**

Signed: *A. Cuyp*

Canvas 71·7 × 100·0

Probably from the early 1650s. (HdG 168)

Purchased by the 4th Marquess of Hertford 1868

P54

**P54   THE FERRY BOAT ON THE MAAS**

Signed: *A. Cuyp*

Panel 71·1 × 89·5

A preliminary drawing is in the print room of the Staatliche Museen, Berlin. (HdG 640)

Purchased by the 4th Marquess of Hertford 1860

**P138   RIVER SCENE WITH VIEW OF DORDRECHT**

Canvas 102·6 × 136·5

Some areas of the painting, e.g. below right, appear to have been retouched, perhaps following an earlier injudicious cleaning. The viewpoint is almost identical with that in P49. (HdG 34, 167b)

Purchased by the 3rd Marquess of Hertford 1811(?)

P138

# After CUYP

## P232 HORSES TIED TO A TREE

Inscribed: *A. Cuyp*

Panel 45·7 × 55·2

A simplified version of a composition by Cuyp (45 × 70) last recorded with Knoedler in 1926. (HdG 552 as Cuyp)

Purchased by the 4th Marquess of Hertford 1861 (through Richard Wallace)

P232

## P250 BOY HOLDING A HORSE

Inscribed: *A. Cuyp*

Panel 40·0 × 31·8

One of three known compositions using the same study of the horse, the best perhaps that in the National Gallery, London, no. 2548, ascribed to Cuyp. Possibly by Jacob van Strij, q.v. (HdG 553, 579, 584 as Cuyp)

Acquired by 1872

P250

## P253 HORSEMEN IN A LANDSCAPE

Inscribed: *A. Cuyp*

Panel 34·3 × 28·6

Possibly a pendant to P255 below and attributable to Jacob van Strij, q.v., cf. P250 above. (HdG 489 as Cuyp)

Acquired by the 3rd Marquess of Hertford by 1834

P253

## P255 A SHEPHERD WITH HIS FLOCK

Inscribed: *A. Cuyp*

Panel 34·3 × 28·6

Possibly a pendant to P253 above and similarly attributable to Jacob van Strij, q.v. (HdG 208 as Cuyp)

Acquired by the 3rd Marquess of Hertford by 1834

P255

# Bernardo DADDI, follower of
### active *c.* 1312–1348

The most important Florentine painter of the earlier 14th century whose pupils and assistants are still being defined.

recto        P549  verso        P549

### P549    THE NATIVITY

Panel 13·3 × 10·8

A fragment, in poor condition, with, *verso*, the truncated body of a male saint carrying a palm of martyrdom in his right hand. Listed by Berenson in 1932 as Daddi, though he then thought the *verso* was perhaps by another hand. A related, larger, composition, also attributed to Daddi, was with Knoedler in 1957.

# Alexandre-Gabriel DECAMPS
### 1803–1860

b. Paris, d. Fontainebleau; travelled in France, Italy and the Middle East; with H. Vernet, q.v., the favourite contemporary artist of the 4th Marquess of Hertford. (Dewey F. Mosby, *Alexandre-Gabriel Decamps 1803–1860*, 2 vols., New York, 1977)

P259

### P259    ARABS REPOSING

Signed: *D.C.*

Canvas 33·0 × 46·7

Dated *c.* 1832–33 by Mosby: lithographed by Laurens. (Mosby 146)

Purchased by the 4th Marquess of Hertford 1867

P261

### P261    THE FINDING OF MOSES

Signed: DECAMPS 1837

Canvas 29·8 × 47·6

The subject is taken from *Exodus* ii, 1–9. Exhibited in the Salon of 1839. (Mosby 152)

Purchased by the 4th Marquess of Hertford 1861

## P263    A WELL IN THE EAST

Signed: DECAMPS 47

Canvas 31·4 × 41·9

Lithographed by Laurens. (Mosby 159 as *Paysage de Syrie*)

Acquired by 1872

P263

## P267    THE VILLA DORIA-PAMPHILI, ROME

Signed: DECAMPS

Canvas 33·0 × 41·3

Exhibited in the Salon of 1839. (Mosby 157)

Purchased by the 4th Marquess of Hertford 1851

P267

## P269    THE BOOKWORM

Signed: DECAMPS 1846

Canvas 21·9 × 27·9

(Mosby 153 as *The Philosopher in his Study*)

Purchased by the 4th Marquess of Hertford 1852

P269

## P292    THE ROMAN CAMPAGNA

Signed: *Decamps*

Panel 24·8 × 41·3

Title inscribed, verso, as *Pifferari et Campagne de Rome*. Dated *c.* 1847 by Mosby. (Mosby 155)

Purchased by the 4th Marquess of Hertford 1853

P292

## P294    THE MIRACULOUS DRAUGHT OF FISHES

Signed: *D.C.*

Canvas 27·9 × 45·7

The subject is taken from *Luke* v, 5–11. Dated *c.* 1853 by Mosby. (Mosby 151)

Purchased by the 4th Marquess of Hertford 1861

P294

P296

**P296   JOSEPH SOLD BY HIS BRETHREN**

Signed: DECAMPS 1838

Canvas 30·8 × 41·6

The subject is taken from *Genesis* xxxvii, 28. Engraved by V. Desclaux. (Mosby 150)

Purchased by the 4th Marquess of Hertford 1843

P302

**P302   ASSES AT BOULAC**

Signed: DECAMPS 1833

Canvas 42·5 × 68·3

Exhibited in the Salon of 1834. Lithographed by Benard and etched by Decamps. (Mosby 147)

Purchased by Sir Richard Wallace 1872

P304

**P304   A JANISSARY**

Initialled: *D*..

Canvas 24·4 × 19·4

Dated 1827 by Mosby; exhibited in the Salon of 1827–8. (Mosby 149)

Purchased by the 4th Marquess of Hertford 1865

**P305   THE WATERING-PLACE**

Signed: DECAMPS

Canvas 80·3 × 117·2

Dated *c.* 1832 by Mosby. A pen and ink sketch, and a preliminary oil sketch, are in Aberdeen Art Gallery. (Mosby 172)

Purchased by the 4th Marquess of Hertford 1851

P305

## P307    THE TURKISH PATROL

Signed: DECAMPS

Canvas 115·3 × 179·4

Exhibited in the Salon 1831 as *Cadji-Bey, chef de la police de Smyrne, faisant sa ronde*. Lithographed by Decamps. A reduced version (75 × 93) is in the Metropolitan Museum, New York. (Mosby 156)

Acquired by the 4th Marquess of Hertford by 1868

P307

## P318    EASTERN WOMEN AT A WELL

Signed: DECAMPS 51

Canvas 33·7 × 42·2

(Mosby 148)

Purchased by the 4th Marquess of Hertford 1853 or 1854

P318

### P345    THE PUNISHMENT OF THE HOOKS

Signed: DECAMPS 1837

Canvas 91·1 × 136·5

Exhibited in the Salon of 1839 as *Le supplice des crochets*, the subject shows thieves hung by their feet from a minaret. (Mosby 154)

Acquired by the 4th Marquess of Hertford by 1857

P345

P350

### P350    THE WITCHES IN MACBETH

Signed: DECAMPS

Canvas 30·5 × 41·3

The subject is probably taken from Shakespeare's *Macbeth* iv, 1. Dated *c.* 1841–2 by Mosby. Lithographed by Eugène Leroux. (Mosby 160)

Purchased by the 4th Marquess of Hertford 1846

P353

### P353    THE ANCHORAGE OF SMYRNA

Signed: *D.C.*

Canvas 46·4 × 67·9

Dated *c.* 1847 by Mosby. (Mosby 145)

Purchased by the 4th Marquess of Hertford 1858

**P649   THE FAVOURITE OF THE PASHA**

Signed: DECAMPS

Water-colour 31·8 × 26·0

Dated *c.* 1830 by Mosby. Lithographed by Garnier. (Mosby 168)

Purchased by the 4th Marquess of Hertford 1860

P649

**P655   CHILDREN GATHERING FLOWERS**

Signed: DECAMPS 44

Water-colour 27·0 × 21·3

(Mosby 166)

Purchased by the 4th Marquess of Hertford 1845

P655

**P660   AN ALBANIAN SENTINEL**

Signed: *Decamps*

Water-colour 28·9 × 24·1

Dated *c.* 1830 by Mosby. (Mosby 162)

Acquired by the 4th Marquess of Hertford by 1868

P660

**P666   AN ALGERIAN WOMAN**

Signed: *Decamps*

Water-colour 45·1 × 36·2

Dated *c.* 1830–32 by Mosby. (Mosby 164)

Purchased by the 4th Marquess of Hertford 1863

P666

P670

### P670   THE READING OF A FIRMAN

Signed: *Decamps*

Water-colour 29·8 × 44·4

A *firman* being an Oriental sovereign's edict. Exhibited in the Salon of 1834. A smaller version (20·6 × 26·5, dated *c.* 1833 by Mosby) was in (Sir) Richard Wallace's sale, Paris, 1857; it is now in the Fodor Museum, Amsterdam. (Mosby 170)

Purchased by the 4th Marquess of Hertford 1846

P677

### P677   ON THE ROOF OF AN ORIENTAL HOUSE

Signed: *Decamps 1830*

Water-colour 22·9 × 23·5

Entitled *An Albanian Family* by Mosby. (Mosby 161)

Purchased by the 4th Marquess of Hertford 1857

P682

### P682   CROSSING THE RIVER

Signed: DECAMPS

Water-colour 32·4 × 46·7

Dated *c.* 1841 by Mosby. A theme treated on several occasions by Decamps. (Mosby 167)

Purchased by the 4th Marquess of Hertford 1860

P692

### P692   OUT OF SCHOOL

Signed: DECAMPS 1841

Water-colour 58·7 × 80·3

Exhibited in the Salon of 1842. Lithographed by Alophe. A version in oils, *Sortie de l'école turque* (66 × 89·5) is in the Louvre. (Mosby 169)

Purchased by the 4th Marquess of Hertford 1861

## P699    ALBANIANS

Signed: *Decamps*

Water-colour 26·0 × 19·7

Dated *c.* 1830 by Mosby. (Mosby 163)

Acquired by the 4th Marquess of Hertford by 1868

P699

## P706    ARABS FORDING A RIVER

Signed: DECAMPS 45

Pastel 48·3 × 83·8

(Mosby 165)

Acquired by 1872

P706

## P717    TOW HORSES

Signed: *Decamps 1830*

Water-colour 21·9 × 31·4

Lithographed by Soulange-Teissler; Mosby gives the original title as *Chevaux de halage.* (Mosby 171)

Purchased by the 4th Marquess of Hertford 1861

P717

## P722    THE WATERING-PLACE

Signed *DECamps*

Water-colour 24·8 × 29·8

Dated *c.* 1832 by Mosby. The right hand side of the composition appears in P259 above. (Mosby 172)

Acquired by the 4th Marquess of Hertford by 1868

P722

# Ferdinand-Victor-Eugène DELACROIX
## 1798–1863

b. Charenton-Saint-Maurice (Val-de-Marne), d. Paris; pupil of Guérin, considerably influenced by Bonington, q.v., Rubens, q.v., and Géricault, q.v.; visited England in 1825, and Morocco and Algiers in 1832; one of the greatest romantic artists; see also Appendix PA2.

### P282    THE EXECUTION OF THE DOGE MARINO FALIERO

Signed: *Eug Delacroix f*[bat]

Canvas 146·4 × 114·3

The subject is taken from Byron's historical tragedy of 1820, *Marino Faliero, Doge of Venice* v, 3 and 4. Faliero was executed in 1355; his headless body lies at the foot of the Giants' Staircase of the Ducal Palace, Venice; a courtier holds his golden robe (left), another his Ducal cap (above); the executioner holds up his bloody sword. Painted in 1826, exhibited in the Salon of 1827–28. P282 was highly regarded by Delacriox himself. Surface cleaned 1977.

Purchased by the 4th Marquess of Hertford 1868

P282

**P324   FAUST AND MEPHISTOPHELES**

Signed: *Eug. Delacroix*

Canvas 46·0 × 38·1

P324

From Goethe's *Faust* i. Exhibited in the Salon of 1827–28 and presented by the artist to Ch. Motte who, in 1828, published seventeen lithographic illustrations to *Faust* after Delacroix designs. P324 was lithographed by Vayron and lettered '*Pourquoi tout ce vacarme? . . .*' (the second scene in Faust's study with Mephistopheles as a travelling scholar, but P324 shows Mephistopheles as a noble squire according to the third scene in Faust's study).

Acquired by 1872

# Hippolyte (Paul) DELAROCHE
## 1797–1856

b. and d. Paris; pupil of Gros, q.v.; achieved a considerable reputation as a history painter. (Norman D. Ziff, *Paul Delaroche*, New York, 1977)

**P276   EDWARD V AND THE DUKE OF YORK IN THE TOWER**

Signed: *Paul de la Roche 1831*

Canvas 43·8 × 51·8

P276

Edward V (1470–83) with his brother Richard, Duke of York (1472–83), were imprisoned in the Tower and murdered by the future Richard III. A replica of the painting in the Louvre (181 × 215, exhibited in the Salon of 1831). (Ziff 49)

Acquired by 1872

**P286   VIRGIN AND CHILD**

Signed: *Paul de la Roche Rome 1844*

Canvas 148·6 × 89·5

Perhaps representing the rest on the flight to Egypt (*Matthew* ii, 13–14), though the distant, apparently departing, figure of Joseph is unusual in this context. (Ziff 129)

Acquired by the 4th Marquess of Hertford by 1857

P286

P300

### P300   JOAN OF ARC IN PRISON

Signed: *De la Roche 1825*

Canvas 46·4 × 37·8

Jeanne d'Arc (1412–31), liberator of Orléans, is interrogated by the Cardinal of Winchester before being condemned and burnt as a heretic by an English tribunal at Rouen. Replica of a painting now in a private collection (376 × 218, exhibited in the Salon of 1824). See also P604 below. (Ziff 16)

Acquired by 1872

P311

### P311   THE TEMPTATION OF ST. ANTHONY

Panel 21·0 × 16·5

Dated *c.* 1832 by Ziff. (Ziff 55)

Purchased by the 4th Marquess of Hertford 1865

P314

### P314   CARDINAL MAZARIN'S LAST SICKNESS

Signed: *Paul De la Roche 1830*

Canvas 57·2 × 97·8

Cardinal Mazarin (1602–61) succeeded Richelieu as *premier ministre* in 1643. Exhibited in the Salon of 1831. (Ziff 42)

Purchased by the 4th Marquess of Hertford 1865

P320

### P320   THE STATE BARGE OF CARDINAL RICHELIEU ON THE RHONE

Signed: *Paul De la Roche 1829*

Canvas 55·2 × 97·8

The subject is suggested by Voltaire's *Essai sur les Moeurs*: the ailing Cardinal takes Cinq-Mars, his former favourite, and de Thou to their execution for conspiracy at Lyon in 1642. Exhibited in the Salon of 1831. See also Robert Fleury, P686, P778. (Ziff 40)

Purchased by the 4th Marquess of Hertford 1865

## P355   A MOTHER'S JOY

Panel 13·7 diameter (painted area)

Dated *c.* 1843 by Ziff. A study for the painting now in the Musée Pescatore, Luxembourg. (Ziff 125)

Acquired by 1872

P355

## P358   A CHILD LEARNING TO READ

Signed: *Paul de la Roche 1848*

Panel 13·7 diameter (painted area)

(Ziff 162)

Acquired by 1872

P358

## P596   THE CONVERSION OF MARY MAGDALENE

Panel 20·0 × 42·5

The subject is taken from *Luke* viii, 1–2. One of six designs prepared for the decoration of the church of the Madeleine, Paris, but not finally executed. Two other lunettes survive in the Hermitage Museum, Leningrad. Dated 1835 by Ziff who also identified the subject of P596 (previously called *Christ on the steps of the temple*) from preparatory drawings now in the Louvre. (Ziff 70)

Acquired by 1872

P596

## P604   JOAN OF ARC IN PRISON

Signed: *P. De la Roche*

Canvas 21·9 × 18·7

Dated *c.* 1824 by Ziff. See P300 above. A study for the larger picture described in that entry. (Ziff 14)

Acquired by 1872

P604

P735

### P735   THE ALCHEMIST

Signed: *Paul de la Roche*

Water-colour 15·9 × 12·4

Acquired by 1874

P738

### P738   THE DEATH OF THE DUC DE GUISE

Signed: *P. de la Roche 1832*

Water-colour 14·6 × 23·8

Henri, duc de Guise (1550–88), popular Catholic commander during the Civil Wars, was assassinated by order of Henri III. A version in oils, executed in 1834, is at Chantilly (57 × 98, exhibited in the Salon of 1835).

Acquired by 1874

## Stephen Poyntz DENNING
### 1795–1864

d. Dulwich; portrait painter and miniaturist; Curator of the Dulwich College Picture Gallery 1821–64.

P765

### P765   QUEEN VICTORIA

Water-colour 39·1 × 30·5

Queen Victoria (1818–1901) ascended the throne in 1837. Copy of the portrait by Sully, dated 1838, in this Collection, P564, q.v., omitting the column on the extreme left.

Purchased by the 4th Marquess of Hertford 1848

# William DERBY
## 1786–1847

b. Birmingham, d. London; portrait painter and copyist.

## P709    THE DUKE OF WELLINGTON

Water-colour 18·4 × 14·0

Arthur Wellesley, 1st Duke of Wellington
(1769–1852), victor of Waterloo and
Conservative statesman. A preparatory study
for an engraving published in *Lodge's Historical
Portraits*, with the inscription: 'From the original by William Evans Esq. Drawn by Wm.
Derby. Engraved by H. T. Ryall, June 1,
1834'. The original portrait appears to derive
from the head painted by Lawrence in 1829;
Evans was Lawrence's pupil.

Purchased by the 4th Marquess of Hertford
1863

P709

## P713    SARAH, DUCHESS OF
##           MARLBOROUGH

Signed: *W. Derby 1823*

Water-colour 18·4 × 14·3

Sarah Jennings (1660–1744), m. John, 1st
Duke of Marlborough, in 1678. A preparatory
study for an engraving published in *Lodge's
Historical Portraits*, with the inscription: 'From
the original of Sir Peter Lely in the collection of
His Grace the Duke of Marlborough. Drawn
by Wm. Derby and engraved by S. Freeman,
June 1, 1834'. The original portrait, in fact by
Maria Verelst *c.* 1725, remains at Blenheim.

Purchased by the 4th Marquess of Hertford
1863

P713

## P725    SARAH, LADY LYNDHURST

Water-colour 28·3 × 23·2

Sarah Brunsden (d. 1834), m. secondly J. S.
Copley (son of the artist of that name), 1st
Baron Lyndhurst, three times Lord
Chancellor, in 1819. Copy of the portrait by
Lawrence, painted in 1828, now in a private
collection.

Purchased by the 4th Marquess of Hertford
1863

P725

# Alexandre-François DESPORTES
## 1661–1743

b. Champigneul, d. Paris; worked in Warsaw as a portrait painter, returned to
Paris by 1699 where he practised as both a portrait and animal painter.

### P594    DOGS, DEAD GAME AND FRUIT

Signed: *Desportes 1715*

Canvas 130·5 × 163·5

Possibly a pendant to P628 below, with which
it was sold in Paris in 1857.

Purchased by the 4th Marquess of Hertford
1857

P594

P623

### P623    TWO DOGS AND DEAD GAME BY
### A FOUNTAIN

Canvas    163·2 × 130·8    extended    to
196·2 × 130·8

The later addition to the top of the composition (the join poorly disguised by a horizontal oak branch) was perhaps an attempt to
make it into a pendant to the Oudry P624, q.v.
Until 1928 attributed to Oudry.

**P628   A DOG WITH FLOWERS AND
           DEAD GAME**

Signed: *Desportes*

Canvas 130·2 × 163·2

Possibly a pendant to P594 above, with which
it was sold in Paris in 1857.

Purchased by the 4th Marquess of Hertford
1857

P628

# Narcisse-Virgilio DIAZ de la Peña
## 1807–1876

b. Bordeaux, d. Menton; began as a decorator of Sèvres porcelain; exhibited at
the Salon from 1831; painted small figure-pieces and landscapes.

**P266   VENUS DISARMING CUPID**

Signed: *N. Diaz*

Panel 19·1 × 12·1

Sketch for a painting, dated 1855, formerly in
the Yerkes collection, New York, and presumably *L'amour puni* sold by Diaz in 1857 and
exhibited in the Salon of 1859, cf. P268 below.

Acquired by 1872

P266

P268

### P268   THE EDUCATION OF CUPID

Signed: *N. Diaz*

Panel 19·1 × 12·1

Presumed to be a sketch for the painting *L'education de l'amour* sold by Diaz in 1857 and exhibited in the Salon of 1859, cf. P266 above.

Acquired by 1872

P312

### P312   A FOUNTAIN AT CONSTANTINOPLE

Signed: *N. Diaz*

Canvas 28·9 × 41·3

Though he frequently exhibited oriental figure and landscape subjects, Diaz is not known to have travelled in the East.

Acquired by 1872

## Christian Wilhelm Ernst DIETRICH

### 1712–1774

b. Weimar, d. Dresden; worked at Dresden where he was Court Painter, Inspector of the Gallery and Director of the Porcelain Manufactory.

P153

### P153   THE CIRCUMCISION

Canvas 52·1 × 70·2

The subject is taken from *Luke* ii, 22–38. The composition is entirely in the manner of early Rembrandt, an artist whom Dietrich greatly admired and often imitated.

# Carlo DOLCI
## 1616–1686

b. and d. Florence; pupil of J. Vignali and M. Rosselli; painted portraits and religious subjects.

### P562   SAINT CATHERINE

Canvas 76·2 × 107·9

The Saint is identified by the crown, one of her attributes since she was reputedly of royal blood; see also Cima P1. Probably painted in the 1650s. A second version is on loan to the Residenzgalerie, Salzburg, from the Schönborn collection, Vienna.

Purchased by the 4th Marquess of Hertford 1865

P562

# DOMENICHINO (Domenico Zampieri)
## 1581–1641

b. Bologna, d. Naples; studied under D. Calvaert and Ludovico Carracci; worked principally in Rome.

### P131   THE PERSIAN SIBYL

Canvas 78·7 × 69·2

A sibyl, a figure of classical mythology, was a woman possessed of prophetic powers, specifically identified by her location (cf. *The Cumaean Sibyl*, Rosa P116). Previously dated 1613–14 on the evidence of three preparatory drawings at Windsor; more recent opinion has favoured a later dating.

Purchased by the 4th Marquess of Hertford 1848

P131

# Gerrit DOU
## 1613–1675

b. and d. Leiden; pupil of Rembrandt, q.v., 1628–*c.* 1632; worked in Leiden where his meticulous style affected many of his pupils (see F. van Mieris, Metsu and Schalcken).

P170

### P170    A HERMIT

Signed: *G. Dou*

Panel 32·1 × 23·8

Originally in a case with doors painted by Dou with still-life subjects. (HdG 24d, 201, 392)

Purchased by the 4th Marquess of Hertford 1843

P177

### P177    A HERMIT AT PRAYER

Panel 41·0 × 29·5

The open book is inscribed: *am funften sontag* (for the fifth Sunday). There is an almost identical version in the Alte Pinakothek, Munich. (HdG 18)

Acquired by 1872

## After DOU

### P168    A GIRL WATERING PLANTS

Panel 31·4 × 20·6

A signed version by Dou (HdG 243) is in the Dresden Gallery. (HdG 209 as Schalcken)

Purchased by the 4th Marquess of Hertford 1849

P168

# John DOWNMAN
## 1750–1824

b. Ruabon (?), d. Wrexham; studied under Benjamin West and in the RA schools; noted for his small crayon portraits.

### P751 ISABELLA, 2nd MARCHIONESS OF HERTFORD, called

Signed: *J.D. 1781*

Tinted drawing 21·0 × 16·5

Isabella Anne Ingram-Shepherd (1760–1834), m. Viscount Beauchamp, later 2nd Marquess of Hertford, in 1776; a favourite of the Prince Regent (George IV). See also P754 below, and Appendix PA3.

Commissioned by the 2nd Marquess of Hertford (?)

P751

### P752 FRANCIS, 3rd MARQUESS OF HERTFORD, AS A CHILD

Signed: *J.D. 1781*

Tinted drawing 21·0 × 16·5

Francis Charles Seymour-Conway (1777–1842), became 3rd Marquess of Hertford in 1822; his red hair was frequently remarked upon. See P754 below.

Commissioned by the 2nd Marquess of Hertford (?)

P752

### P753 FRANCES, LADY WILLIAM GORDON

Signed: *J. Downman: P. 1783*

Tinted drawing 21·0 × 16·5

Frances Ingram-Shepherd (1761–1841), younger sister of Isabella (see P751 above), m. Lord William Gordon in 1781.

Commissioned by the 2nd Marquess of Hertford (?)

P753

P754

## P754   ELIZABETH INGRAM-SHEPHERD, called

Signed: *J.D. 1781*

Tinted drawing 21·0 × 16·5

Tentatively identified as Elizabeth Ingram-Shepherd (*c.* 1762–1817), younger sister of Isabella and Frances (see P751 and P753 above), m. Hugo Meynell in 1782. Four other versions are recorded; one has been known as 'Miss Way', two others are inscribed by the artist as being of 'Lady Beauchamp' (i.e. Isabella, P751); one of these two is further inscribed 'I drew three of this and her little boy' (i.e. P752).

Commissioned by the 2nd Marquess of Hertford (?)

# Willem DROST, attributed to
active 1652–after 1654

An artist of whom very little is known; presumed to have been a pupil of Rembrandt, evidently also influenced by F. Bol, q.v., and B. van der Helst, q.v.

P61

## P61   A YOUNG WOMAN

Canvas 62·9 × 50·8

A false inscription, apparently reading *Rembrandt ft.*, was removed in cleaning 1976. Probably painted in the 1650s.

Purchased by Sir Richard Wallace 1872

# Gaspard DUGHET
## 1615–1675

b. and d. Rome; brother-in-law of Nicolas Poussin, q.v., of whom he was a pupil *c.* 1630 for more than three years; decorative and landscape painter, active mainly in Rome.

### P139 THE FALLS OF TIVOLI

Canvas 100·3 × 83·5

Probably painted *c.* 1665–66; engraved by J. Mason 1744 when in Lord Waldegrave's collection, together with a pendant, also a view of Tivoli. Cleaned 1978.

Purchased by the 4th Marquess of Hertford 1850

P139

# Jules DUPRÉ
## 1811–1889

b. Nantes, d. L'Isle-Adam; initially influenced by the 17th-century Dutch landscapists Ruisdael and Hobbema, q.v.; one of the Barbizon school.

### P299 CROSSING THE BRIDGE

Signed: *Jules Dupré 1838*

Canvas 49·5 × 64·8

In 1900 P299 was described as 'A scene on the river Pay' (*sic*); possibly the picture exhibited in the Salon of 1839 as *Pont sur la rivière du Fay.*

Acquired by 1872

P299

# Anthony van DYCK
## 1599–1641

b. Antwerp, d. London; assisted Rubens, q.v.; worked in England 1620–21 and 1632–41, in Italy 1621–28, and in Antwerp 1628–32; particularly admired for his portraiture; knighted by Charles I 1632; see also Titian P11.

P16

### P16   ISABELLA WAERBEKE

Canvas 120·7 × 95·9

The sitter m. Paul de Vos, whose companion portrait was burnt in 1890. From the second Antwerp period 1628–32. See also de Vos P22.

Purchased by the 4th Marquess of Hertford 1848

P79

### P79   MARIE DE RAET

Inscribed: AET. SVAE 16. A. 1631

Canvas 214·0 × 123·2

The sitter m. Philippe le Roy (see P94 below) in 1631, when she was sixteen, the year P79 was painted. Traces of a now illegible coat of arms appear top right.

Purchased by the 4th Marquess of Hertford 1850

## P85  THE ARTIST AS THE SHEPHERD PARIS

Canvas 104·8 × 91·8

Holding the golden apple in his right hand, the artist presents himself as Paris, the judge of beauty (cf. Boucher P444). From the Italian period 1621–28.

Purchased by the 3rd Marquess of Hertford 1816

P85

## P94  PHILIPPE LE ROY, SEIGNEUR DE RAVELS

Signed: A VAN DYCK, F and inscribed: AETATIS SVAE 34 A° 1630

Canvas 214·6 × 123·2

Philippe Le Roy (c.1596–?after 1671), was counsellor to the Archduke Ferdinand, Governor of the Netherlands, and created Baron of Broechen and of the Holy Roman Empire in 1671. Painted the year before his marriage to Marie de Raet, see P79 above. A now illegible coat of arms appears top left.

Purchased by the 4th Marquess of Hertford 1850

P94

P53

# Follower of van DYCK

## P53   YOUNG ITALIAN NOBLEMAN

Canvas 205·7 × 135·9

Probably by a Genoese artist imitating van Dyck's Italian manner; an attribution to van Dyck himself was doubted as early as 1822.

Acquired by the 4th Marquess of Hertford by 1856

P112

# After van DYCK

## P112   KING CHARLES I

Canvas 124·5 × 99·1

Charles I (1600–49) ascended the throne in 1625 and suffered execution at Whitehall. One of many copies from van Dyck's full-length portrait at Windsor painted in 1636.

In the collection of the 3rd Marquess of Hertford

P118

## P118   QUEEN HENRIETTA MARIA

Canvas 124·5 × 99·1

Henrietta Maria (1609–66), daughter of Henri IV of France, m. Charles I in 1625; she died in Paris. One of many copies from a van Dyck pattern of *c.* 1632, closely related to a half-length at Windsor but differing in having the rose in the left hand.

In the collection of the 3rd Marquess of Hertford

**P123   THE VIRGIN AND CHILD**

Canvas 108·3 × 83·5

Copied from a painting by van Dyck at Buckingham Palace which has been dated *c.* 1630–32.

Purchased by the 4th Marquess of Hertford 1845

P123

# Allart van EVERDINGEN
## 1621–1675

b. Alkmaar, d. Amsterdam; worked in Haarlem and Amsterdam, travelled in Norway and Sweden 1640–44; his lively water scenes influenced Jacob van Ruisdael, q.v.

**P113   LANDSCAPE WITH WATERFALL**

Canvas 85·7 × 66·7

Purchased by Sir Richard Wallace 1872

P113

# Hans EWORTH, follower of
## active 1540–1574

Antwerp artist, working in London 1549–1572

P535

## P535   JOHN SELWYN (?)

Inscribed: HE and AETATIS 54 1572

Panel 86·4 × 62·9

The age and date, together with a coat of arms revealed in cleaning 1978 (all, however, additions to the original portrait) identify John Selwyn of Friston, Sussex, whose son, Thomas, was granted the coat of arms in 1611. A later inscription, *Robertus Co: Leicestriae*, was removed in cleaning. A version at Parham Park is inscribed *1568 Aet 51* and called the 3rd Earl of Worcester.

In the collection of the 3rd Marquess of Hertford

# Jean-Baptiste FAUVELET
## 1819–1883

b. Bordeaux, d. Chartres; a follower of Meissonier, q.v.

P374

## P374   PHEASANTS

Signed: *Fauvelet*

Panel 16·8 × 21·6

Acquired by 1872

# FERRARESE SCHOOL
## late XVth century

P536

## P536   THE ANNUNCIATION

Plaster, two panels each 43·8 × 14·0

The subject is taken from *Luke* i, 28. The two panels are probably fragments of a larger composition, the middle section being lost.

# Anthony Vandyke Copley FIELDING
## 1787–1855

b. East Sowerby, d. Worthing; influenced by John Varley.

**P690  LANGDALE PIKES, WESTMORLAND**

Signed: *Copley Fielding 1839*

Water-colour 45·7 × 61·6

Purchased by the 4th Marquess of Hertford 1863

P690

**P691  BRIDLINGTON HARBOUR**

Signed: *Copley Fielding 1837*

Water-colour 47·6 × 78·7

Purchased by the 4th Marquess of Hertford 1863

P691

**P715  CROWBOROUGH HILL, SUSSEX**

Signed: *Copley Fielding 1838*

Water-colour 42·4 × 60·0

Purchased by the 4th Marquess of Hertford 1863

P715

**P716  LOCH KATRINE**

Signed: *Copley Fielding 1839*

Water-colour 31·1 × 41·3

Purchased by the 4th Marquess of Hertford 1863

P716

P718

### P718   TRAETH MAWR, NORTH WALES

Signed: *Copley Fielding 1838*

Water-colour 42·9 × 60·0

Purchased by the 4th Marquess of Hertford 1863

# FLEMISH SCHOOL
## second quarter XVIth century

P529

### P529   THE EMPEROR CHARLES V

Panel 15·2 × 11·7

Charles V (1500–58), King of Spain 1516–56, Holy Roman Emperor 1519–58. P529 was probably adapted from a three-quarter length portrait, formerly in the collection of King Louis-Philippe, engraved by Holl as Henry VIII by Holbein. See also Bonington P727, Robert-Fleury P361, and *Catalogue of Sculpture* S400 and S408.

## Govaert FLINCK
### 1615–1660

b. Cleves, d. Amsterdam; pupil of L. Jacobsz at Leeuwarde, and of Rembrandt at Amsterdam. See also Rembrandt, Follower, P201. (J. W. von Moltke, *Govaert Flinck*, Amsterdam, 1965)

### P238   A YOUNG NEGRO ARCHER

Panel 67·6 × 51·8

Traces of a signature remain below the bow on the right. Dated 1639–40 by von Moltke. The same bow, quiver and baldric appear in the artist's self-portrait in the National Gallery of South Africa, Capetown. (von Moltke 180; HdG 267 as Rembrandt)

Purchased by the 4th Marquess of Hertford 1848

P238

# FLORENTINE SCHOOL
## last quarter 15th century

### P556  AN ALLEGORY OF LOVE

Panel 61·6 × 77·2

The subject has been interpreted as showing Cupid bound, consumed by the flames of love while on an altar drawn by two winged horses, bidden by Venus who holds Cupid's bow. P556 belongs to a group of paintings apparently by the same hand, the most important being three altarpieces in S. Spirito, Florence, and a tondo in the National Gallery, London, no. 2492.

P556

### P768  VIRGIN AND CHILD

Panel 15·2 diameter

An old attribution to Ghirlandaio (whose name is inscribed on the verso) is untenable.

P768

## Vincenzo FOPPA
### active 1456 d.1515/16

Worked in Pavia c. 1456–90, then in Brescia where he died.

### P538  THE YOUNG CICERO READING

Fresco on plaster 99·1 × 133·0

Cicero, the celebrated Roman orator, is portrayed as a model of schoolboy industry; he is identified by the inscription on the wall *M.T. Cicero*. Originally part of a series of frescoes commissioned by Cosimo dei Medici for the Banco Mediceo, Milan, painted by Foppa in the 1460s; the theme was possibly that of great men from antiquity. P538 was removed from the Banco after 1862, and was then the sole surviving fragment.

Purchased by Sir Richard Wallace 1872 (?)

P538

# Jean-Honoré FRAGONARD
## 1732–1806

b. Grasse, d. Paris; pupil of Boucher, q.v., 1750–52, and of Carle van Loo, q.v., 1752–56; travelled in Italy 1756–61 (with Hubert Robert and the abbé de Saint-Non) and 1773; influenced by Dutch 17th-century landscape and portraiture, particularly Rembrandt; a painter of great individuality who died neglected. (See also *Catalogue of Miniatures*, M110)

P379

### P379   THE GARDENS OF THE VILLA D'ESTE, TIVOLI

Canvas 37·5 × 46·4

Engraved by the artist 1763 as *Le petit parc*, and probably painted soon after his return from Italy, *c.* 1762; one of a number of novel, richly poetical studies in which nature dominates tiny figures.

Acquired by 1872

P382

### P382   THE SOUVENIR

Inscribed: *fragonard*

Panel 26·7 × 20·3

A slightly reduced version of a lost original (32 × 24) painted 1773–76 and engraved by N. Delaunay as *Le chiffre d'amour*.

Purchased by the 4th Marquess of Hertford 1865

P394

### P394   THE FOUNTAIN OF LOVE

Signed: *Fragonard*

Canvas 64·1 × 51·8

Engraved in 1785 as *La fontaine d'amour* and probably executed immediately before that date. A late work remarkable for its classical restraint in colour and form.

Purchased by the 4th Marquess of Hertford 1870

## P404   THE SCHOOLMISTRESS

Signed: *Fragonard* (within the alphabet on the blackboard)

Canvas 29·2 × 37·5

A similar composition was engraved by N. Delaunay as *Dîtes donc s'il vous plaît* in 1783.

Purchased by the 4th Marquess of Hertford 1841

P404

## P412   A BOY AS PIERROT

Canvas 61·0 × 50·8

Probably painted after 1789. A pendant, *La jeune fille au collier de perles*, was last sold in New York in 1962. Acquired as by Boucher.

Purchased by Sir Richard Wallace 1872

P412

## P430   THE SWING

Canvas 82·9 × 66·0

The subject was devised by the Baron de Saint-Julien who had previously commissioned Doyen to paint it, but he refused; the Baron (left) eyes his mistress on the swing which is worked by an older man (he had first specified that this should be a bishop). Painted 1768–69, and engraved 1782 by N. Delaunay as *Les hazards heureux de l'escarpolette*.

Purchased by the 4th Marquess of Hertford 1865

P430

P455

## P455   A YOUNG SCHOLAR

Signed: *frago...*

Canvas 45·7 × 38·1

Painted *c.* 1773–6; a Dutch influence is here apparent.

Purchased by Sir Richard Wallace 1872

P471

## P471   THE MUSICAL CONTEST

Canvas 72·4 × 108·6

Previously attributed to Boucher (the initials *f.B* can doubtfully be read, bottom left), an attribution to Fragonard was verbally accepted by Georges Wildenstein. An early work much influenced by Boucher, probably dating from 1750–52.

## P483   CUPIDS AT PLAY

Canvas 97·2 × 144·1

Dated 1750–52 by Wildenstein. Pendant to P488 below; both pictures were at one time attributed to Boucher.

Acquired by 1874

P483

**P488    CUPIDS ASLEEP**

Canvas 97·5 × 142·2

See P483 above.

Acquired by 1874

P488

# FRANCESCO di Vanuccio
## active 1361–1388

Sienese artist; there is a *Crucifixion* by him, signed and dated 1361, in Berlin.

**P550    VIRGIN AND CHILD WITH SS
PETER AND JOHN THE BAPTIST**

Panel 54·6 × 25·4

Listed by Berenson as the left wing of a triptych.

P550

# FRENCH SCHOOL
*c.* 1790–1800

P599

### P599   CHARLES JOSEPH, PRINCE DE LIGNE

Canvas 19·4 × 15·2

Charles Joseph, prince de Ligne (1735–1814), soldier, wit and author, lived in the château de Boloeil, near Mons. A label, verso, states that P599 is a sketch painted at Boloeil; a finished version is not known.

Acquired by 1872

# Jan FYT
1611–1661

b. and d. Antwerp; pupil of F. Snijders, q.v.; worked in Paris 1633–34, and in Rome and Venice before returning to Antwerp in 1641; painted accessories for both Rubens, q.v., and Jordaens, q.v.

### P101   STILL LIFE WITH A PAGE

Signed: *Joannes FYT 1644*

Canvas 123·2 × 206·7

Acquired by 1872

P101

# Thomas GAINSBOROUGH
1727–1788

b. Sudbury, d. London; pupil of Gravelot in London *c.* 1740 to *c.* 1746; worked in Sudbury 1746–52, Ipswich 1752–59, Bath 1759–74 and London from 1774; a most successful, but reluctant, portraitist, he also painted landscapes and genre scenes.

### P42   MRS MARY ROBINSON ('PERDITA')

Canvas 228·6 × 153·0

Mary Darby (1758–1800) m. Thomas Robinson 1774; achieved fame as an actress 1776–80 and as a favourite of the Prince of Wales 1779–80; crippled after a miscarriage 1783, she took to writing poetry and novels. Painted for the Prince of Wales between August and October 1781, the miniature in her right hand thought to refer to that he gave her of himself (by Meyer). See also Reynolds P45, Romney P37 and *Catalogue of Miniatures* M40.

Presented by the Prince Regent to the 2nd Marquess of Hertford 1818

P42

### P44   MISS HAVERFIELD

Canvas 127·6 × 101·9

The identification is traditional, the painting being sold by the family in 1859; probably the daughter of John Haverfield, Superintendant of Kew Gardens 1784–95; she m. the Rev. J. Wyld. Painted in the 1780s.

Purchased by the 4th Marquess of Hertford 1859

P44

# Louis GALLAIT
## 1810–1887

b. Tournai, d. Brussels; studied in Antwerp and Paris, much influenced by Delaroche, q.v.

P308

**P308 THE DUKE OF ALVA ADMINISTERING AN OATH**

Signed: *Louis Gallait 1855*

Canvas 101·0 × 82·2

According to a sale-catalogue description from 1863, the oath is being taken by Juan de Vargas, the notorious arbiter of the *Council of the Blood* instituted by the Duke of Alva (1508–82) to suppress the Spanish Netherlands.

Purchased by the 4th Marquess of Hertford 1863

# Jean-Louis-André-Théodore GÉRICAULT
## 1791–1824

b. Rouen, d. Paris; studied under Carle Vernet and Guérin; visited Italy 1816–17 and London 1820–22; with Delacroix, q.v., one of the great romantic artists of the early 19th century.

P274

**P274 A CAVALRY SKIRMISH**

Canvas 38·1 × 46·4

Probably painted between 1812 and 1816. Lithographed by Volmar 1824 as *Cuirassiers enlevant un drapeau à des Russes*.

Purchased by the 4th Marquess of Hertford 1857

**P755    KING GEORGE IV AS A
GENERAL OFFICER OF
HUSSARS**

Water-colour 30·5 × 25·4

For George IV, see Hoppner P563 and
Lawrence P559. A copy, with improvements,
of a portrait by G. H. Harlow (painted *c.*1810
and engraved by W. Ward) which Géricault
probably saw in London between 1820 and
1822.

Acquired by 1872

P755

# GERMAN SCHOOL
## mid 16th century

**P533    A BOY WITH A NOSEGAY**

Inscribed: A⸰ DÑI. 1560

Panel 41·6 × 31·1

An attribution to Jacob Seisenegger (1505–67)
has been suggested.

P533

# Jean-Léon GÉRÔME
## 1824–1904

b. Vesoul, Haute-Saone, d. Paris; pupil of Delaroche, q.v.; visited Greece and Turkey 1854 and paid regular visits to Egypt between 1856 and 1875.

**P301    THE DRAUGHT PLAYERS**
Signed: J.L. GEROME 1859
Panel 43·2 × 28·9
Acquired by 1872

P301

**P306    THE GUARD OF THE HAREM**
Signed: J.L. GEROME 1859
Panel 23·8 × 14·9
Acquired by 1872

P306

# Jean-Baptiste GREUZE
## 1725–1805

b. Tournus, d. Paris; studied in Lyon with Ch. Grandon between 1745–50; came to Paris 1750, where he studied under Natoire at the Académie; travelled in Italy 1755–57; exhibited regularly at the Salon from 1755 to 1769 when a quarrel over his *morceau de réception* (*L'Empereur Sévère*, Louvre), led to his withdrawal until 1800; his later work was dominated by the expressive heads of girls; noted for his moral genre scenes, a mode of *sensibilité* he outlived.

## P384   INNOCENCE

Panel 63·2 × 51·8

Painted in the 1790s. Three other versions, and
a preparatory drawing, are recorded.

Acquired by 1872

P384

## P388   PSYCHE

Inscribed, verso: *J.B. Greuze 1786*

Panel 45·4 × 37·5

For another preparatory version, see P440
below.

Purchased by the 4th Marquess of Hertford
1857

P388

## P396   HEAD OF A BOY

Canvas 40·0 × 31·8

Painted *c.* 1782. Previously known as
*Espièglerie (The Mischief-Maker)*.

Acquired by 1872

P396

P398

### P398   THE SOUVENIR OF FIDELITY

Signed: *Greuze*

Canvas 53·3 × 44·5

Painted *c.* 1789. Relates closely to *La colombe retrouvée* in the Pushkin Museum, Moscow, which is dated 1789.

Acquired by 1872

P402

### P402   THE LISTENING GIRL

Panel 48·3 × 39·4

Acquired by 1872

P403

### P403   MLLE. SOPHIE ARNOULD, called

Canvas 62·5 × 51·8

Painted *c.* 1786, P403 was not acquired as a portrait of Mlle. Arnould (1744–1803, singer, actress and wit, who appeared on the Paris stage between 1758 and 1778). A marble bust of her by Houdon, formerly in The Wallace Collection, is now in the Louvre.

Purchased by the 4th Marquess of Hertford 1858

## P407   BACCHANTE

Canvas 46·0 × 38·1

Probably dates from the 1780s. Another version is at Waddesdon.

Purchased by the 4th Marquess of Hertford 1857(?)

P407

## P413   A LADY

Canvas 50·5 × 39·7

Unfinished; probably painted *c.*1770.

Acquired by 1872

P413

## P415   GIRL WITH A GAUZE SCARF

Canvas 57·8 × 47·0

Painted *c.* 1770.

Acquired by 1872

P415

P419

**P419   BOY WITH A DOG**

Canvas 61·0 × 51.4

Painted *c.* 1760. A copy, without the dog, is at Waddesdon; a copy in miniature was in the J. Pierpont Morgan collection.

Acquired by 1872

P421

**P421   ARIADNE**

Panel 49·5 × 42·5

Probably exhibited in the Salon of 1804; a very late work. Greuze explained that the 'crown of stars' indicated that sentiment 'makes us momentarily the equals of the gods'.

Purchased by the 4th Marquess of Hertford 1849

P425

**P425   GIRL IN A BLUE DRESS**

Panel 40·3 × 33·0

A very late work, probably *c.* 1804–5. The dress is Spanish in style.

Acquired by 1872

## P427    GIRL IN A WHITE DRESS

Canvas 46·4 × 38·7

Possibly exhibited in the Salon of 1765.

Purchased by the 4th Marquess of Hertford
1845

P427

## P428    GIRL WITH DOVES

Signed: *J.B. Greuze*

Panel 69·9 × 58·7

Painted in 1802, on the evidence of a dated
receipt, signed by the artist, for 4.800 *livres*
from a Monsieur Wilkinson, *verso*. A copy of
P428 was made in 1831 by John Constable
(commissioned as a memorial to a dead child).
The model has been identified as Mme.
Dupuy, mother of the French press baron,
Émile de Girardin (1806–81), but this seems
doubtful.

Purchased by the 4th Marquess of Hertford
1848

P428

## P434    FLYING CUPID WITH A TORCH

Panel 27·3 × 22·2

Probably from the early 1780s, the figure
recalling the Cupid in *L'Innocence entraînée par
les Amours* (Louvre).

Acquired by 1872

P434

P440

**P440  PSYCHE**

Panel 41·0 × 33·0

See P388 above; P440 has a slightly more agonised look.

Purchased by the 4th Marquess of Hertford 1846

P441

**P441  THE VOTIVE OFFERING TO CUPID**

Canvas 147·3 × 111·4

The young girl, dressed in 'Greek' costume, prays to the God of Love who stands on a plinth which bears a bas-relief of Pan and Syrinx (Ovid, *Metamorphoses* i). The subject was also painted by Vien and Louis-Michel van Loo, q.v., in the 1760s. P441 was painted *c.* 1767 and exhibited in the Salon of 1769 when the drawing of the girl was particularly criticised.

Purchased by the 4th Marquess of Hertford 1845

P442

**P442  THE BROKEN MIRROR**

Canvas 55·9 × 45·7

A moral genre scene, showing the effects of slovenliness. Listed as exhibited in the Salon of 1763, but not shown. A drawing for the dog is in the Hermitage Museum, Leningrad.

Purchased by the 4th Marquess of Hertford 1845

## P443   GIRL LEANING ON HER HAND

Canvas 46·4 × 38·7

Probably painted *c.* 1800; compare P459 below.

Acquired by 1872

P443

## P454   THE INCONSOLABLE WIDOW

Canvas 41·9 × 34·3

A sentimental genre scene, inviting the spectator to share the widow's pious grief. Listed as exhibited in the Salon of 1763, but not shown.

Acquired by 1872

P454

## P459   THE LETTER WRITER

Signed: *Greuze*

Canvas 40·6 × 33·0

Painted *c.* 1800; probably the picture exhibited in the Salon of 1800 as *Une jeune femme se disposant à écrire une lettre d'amour.* Another version was recently on the London art market. See also P443 above.

Acquired by 1872

P459

# Antoine-Jean Baron GROS
## 1771–1835

b. Paris, d. Meudon; pupil of David; went to Italy 1792 where he met Napoleon with whom he found considerable favour; returned to France 1800; created *baron* by Charles X.

P303

### P303  GENERAL BONAPARTE REVIEWING TROOPS

Signed: *Gros fe*

Canvas 40·3 × 32·4

The composition recalls the central motif of *Le général Bonaparte passant une revue après la bataille de Marengo*, painted in 1802 (Compiègne).

Acquired by 1872

# Francesco GUARDI
## 1712–1793

b. and d. Venice; trained with his elder brother, G. A. Guardi (1698–1760) as a history painter; turned to painting views of Venice *c.* 1755–60, displaying a more lyrical (and less topographical) interest than Canaletto, q.v. (A. Morassi, *Guardi*, 2 vols., Venice, 1973)

P491

### P491  SAN GIORGIO MAGGIORE

Canvas 71·4 × 94·3

A view from the north west, with the Giudecca to the right. A pendant to P494, P503 and P508, see below; the set was apparently acquired in Russia by the duc de Morny in the mid-19th century. All four pictures have been extended, and originally measured *c.* 68 × 91; they were probably painted in the 1770s. P491 is one of the finest of many versions by Guardi of the same subject, see also P517 below. (Morassi 432)

Purchased by the 4th Marquess of Hertford 1865

## P494   THE DOGANA

Canvas 71·4 × 94·3

A view from the north, the Giudecca with the church of the Redentore in the distance. See P491. (Morassi 505)

Purchased by the 4th Marquess of Hertford 1865

P494

## P502   AN ARCHITECTURAL CAPRICE

Panel 27·6 × 21·9

A caprice of Venetian architecture, probably painted after 1780. Pendant to P504 below, and possibly a picture at Lyons (27 × 22, Morassi 799); this set is matched by a similar but larger set (rectangular c. 54 × 36; two in a private collection, one in the National Gallery, London no. 2523; Morassi, under 776, and 784). (Morassi 814)

Acquired by 1872

P502

## P503   SANTA MARIA DELLA SALUTE

Canvas 71·4 × 94·3

From the north west, the Abbazia di S. Gregorio to the right. See P491 above. (Morassi 487)

Purchased by the 4th Marquess of Hertford 1865

P503

## P504   AN ARCHITECTURAL CAPRICE

Panel 27·6 × 21·9

A caprice of Venetian architecture embodying features from the lower arcade of the Doge's Palace. See P502 above. A second version is in the Gulbenkian Foundation, Lisbon. (Morassi 779).

Acquired by 1872

P504

P508

## P508   THE RIALTO

Canvas 71·4 × 94·3

From the south west, the Riva del Vin on the left (cf. Canaletto P511). See P491 above. (Morassi 528)

Purchased by the 4th Marquess of Hertford 1865

P517

## P517   SAN GIORGIO MAGGIORE

Canvas 39·1 × 55·2

From the north west, cf. P491 above. Probably dates from the 1770s. (Morassi 429)

Acquired by 1872

P518

## P518   THE DOGANA WITH SANTA MARIA DELLA SALUTE

Canvas 35·6 × 55·6

From the north east, with the Abbazia di S. Gregorio on the right. A late work, of which there are also good versions in Birmingham City Art Gallery and the Museum of Fine Arts, Boston (oval). (Morassi 481)

Acquired by 1872

P647

## P647   AN ARCHITECTURAL CAPRICE

Canvas 39·4 × 29·5

A caprice of Venetian architecture embodying the courtyard of the Ducal Palace and the Giants' Staircase (see Delacroix P282). Probably from the 1770s. A close version is in the National Gallery, London, no. 2519. (Morassi 789)

Purchased by the 4th Marquess of Hertford 1859

# Théodore-Jean-Antoine GUDIN
## 1802–1880

b. Paris, d. Boulogne; pupil of Girodet-Trioson; marine painter to King Louis-Philippe, painting over eighty subjects for Versailles; spent much of his later life in Scotland.

### P580   A STORM AT SEATON

Signed: *T. Gudin Seaton N.B. 1846*

Canvas 90·2 × 127·6

Presumably the location is Seaton Sluice, Northumberland (and not Seaton, Devon). Possibly exhibited in the Salon of 1846 or 1847.

Acquired by 1872

P580

# Johannes HACKAERT
## *c.* 1629–1685 or after

b. Amsterdam; travelled in Switzerland and Italy 1653–58.

### P121   AN AVENUE IN A WOOD

Signed: J. HACKAERT

Canvas 62·9 × 52·1

Related versions are in the Petit Palais, Paris, and the Rijksmuseum, Amsterdam. (HdG 41, the figures said to be by Adriaen van de Velde)

Purchased by the 4th Marquess of Hertford 1865

P121

### P245   THE WOODED BANKS OF A RIVER

Canvas 63·5 × 47·6

(HdG 81, the figures said to be by Johannes Lingelbach)

Purchased by the 4th Marquess of Hertford 1845(?)

P245

# Frans HALS
## *c.* 1580(?)–1666

b. probably Antwerp, d. Haarlem; came to Haarlem before 1591 and worked there the rest of his life; pupil of Karel van Mander; particularly renowned for his vivacious portraits. (S. Slive, *Frans Hals*, vol. 3 catalogue, 1974)

P84

### P84   THE LAUGHING CAVALIER

Inscribed: AETA. SVAE 26 / A° 1624

Canvas 85·7 × 68·6

Though neither laughing, nor, strictly, a cavalier, this elegant twenty-six year old is deservedly famous as the subject of an outstanding baroque portrait. The present title was probably earned in the course of its exhibition at Bethnal Green between 1872 and 1875. The jacket is richly embroidered with emblems (of virtue, of the God Mercury, and of love, for example) which are probably decorative, rather than collectively emblematic. (HdG 291; Slive 30)

Purchased by the 4th Marquess of Hertford 1865

# James Duffield HARDING
## 1798–1863

b. Deptford, d. Barnes; pupil of Samuel Prout; water-colourist and lithographer.

### P658   BERNKASTEL ON THE MOSELLE

Water-colour 77·2 × 105·4

Purchased by the 4th Marquess of Hertford 1863

P658

# Silvester HARDING
## 1745–1809

b. Newcastle-under-Lyme, d. London; miniaturist, portraitist and copyist; compiled, with his brother Edward, the anthology of historical portraits, the *Biographical Mirrour* (1795–98).

### P770   ANN, 5th VISCOUNTESS IRWIN

Signed and inscribed: *S. Harding del 1801 C. Phillips* (sic) *pinxt 1738* THE LADY ANN DAUGHTER TO THE / EARL OF CARLISLE, VISCOUNTESS DOWAGER / IRWIN AND WIDOW OF THE LATE / BRIGADIER WILLIAM DOUGLAS / DIED DEC$^r$ 4, 1764

Water-colour 19·7 × 15·9

P770

Ann, daughter of the 3rd Earl of Carlisle and a poetess, m. 1st in 1718 Richard Ingram, 5th Viscount Irwin (d. 1721), and 2nd in 1737 Col. James (*sic*) Douglas. For some of her indirect descendants, see Downman P751, P753 and P754. The original portrait by Philips remains untraced today, though portraits of the sitter by Richardson and Dandridge are at Temple Newsam.

Acquired by the 2nd Marquess of Hertford (?)

# Henry Andrew HARPER
## 1835–1900

b. Blunham, Beds.; painted views of Egypt and the East and published books on Palestine and the Bible.

### P694   THE JEWS' WAILING PLACE, JERUSALEM

Signed: *Henry A. Harper 1874* and inscribed with title.

Water-colour 33·7 × 67·6

Exhibited at the RA in 1874

Acquired by Sir Richard Wallace

P694

### P695   THE NILE AT CAIRO

Signed: *Henry A. Harper 1874*

Water-colour 48·3 × 73·0

Acquired by Sir Richard Wallace

P695

# Jan Davidsz de HEEM
## 1605/6–1683/4

b. Utrecht, d. Antwerp; pupil of his father David de Heem; worked in Leyden, Utrecht and, after 1671, at Antwerp.

### P76　STILL LIFE WITH MONKEY

*attributed to J.J. de Heem 1650-1685*

Signed: DE HEEM F

Canvas 120·7 × 171·8

Purchased by the 4th Marquess of Hertford 1859(?)

P76

### P107　STILL LIFE WITH FRUIT AND PARROT

Signed: *J.D.De Heem*

Canvas 128·0 × 139·7

Originally called de Heem, but attributed to Pieter de Ring in 1904 until the present; there seems no reason to doubt the signature which has not previously been recorded; the ring (extreme right) might indicate the collaboration of de Ring, who was a pupil of de Heem.

Acquired by 1872

P107

**P175    STILL LIFE WITH A LOBSTER**

Signed: *J. De Heem f.*

Canvas 79·4 × 103·8

Purchased by the 4th Marquess of Hertford
1843

P175

# Ferdinand HEILBUTH
## 1826–1889

b. Hamburg, d. Paris; worked in Rome and Paris, becoming a French citizen; a
friend of Sir Richard Wallace.

**P342    EXCAVATIONS IN ROME**

Signed: *F. Heilbuth*

Canvas 86·0 × 150·2

Acquired by Sir Richard Wallace by 1878

P342

**P576    THE CARDINAL**

Signed: *F. Heilbuth*

Canvas 72·1 × 124·5

Listed in 1897 as *Boy kissing the Cardinal's hand
on Monte Pincio*. Heilbuth was known in Rome
as the 'Painter of Cardinals'.

Acquired by Sir Richard Wallace by 1878

P576

# Bartholomeus van der HELST
## 1613?–1670

b. Haarlem, d. Amsterdam; worked in Amsterdam from at least 1636; a founder of the Amsterdam Guild 1653 and a portrait painter of distinction.

### P110    A FAMILY GROUP

Signed: *Van der Helst f. 1654*

Canvas 170·8 × 198·4

Acquired by 1872

P110

# Jan van der HEYDEN
## 1637–1712

b. Gorinchem, d. Amsterdam; moved to Amsterdam by 1650; painter of townscapes, sometimes fancifully assembled; engaged in the study of fire-fighting and street-lighting from the late 1660s. (H. Wagner, *Jan van der Heyden*, Amsterdam, 1971)

P195

### P195    A STREET SCENE IN COLOGNE

Panel 31·4 × 40·3

The crane on the tower of the cathedral (which is seen from the west) was positioned by the second half of the 15th century; the tower remained as shown until 1868 when the crane was finally removed. A comparable view, apparently more topographically exact, is in the National Gallery, London, no. 866. The figures in P195 were attributed by de Groot to

Adriaen van de Velde, q.v. (HdG 88, Wagner 45)

Purchased by the 3rd Marquess of Hertford 1807

## P225    VIEW OF THE WESTERKERK, AMSTERDAM

Signed: *J.V.D. Heyden*

Panel 41·3 × 59·0

The position of the steeple has been changed and the space before the church exaggerated. The figures, boat and water, were attributed to Adriaen van de Velde, q.v., in the 1848 Duval sale catalogue. (HdG 14, noting the supposed contribution of van de Velde; Wagner 7)

P225

Purchased by the 4th Marquess of Hertford 1848

## P230    EXTERIOR OF A CHURCH

Signed: *JV Heyden*

Panel 45·7 × 60·0

De Groot thought the church was possibly that of the Carmelites at Cologne; he also noted that the 'unfinished tower' to the left was a free rendering of a part of the Nieuwe Kerk at Amsterdam. The figures have been attributed to Adriaen van de Velde, q.v. (HdG 160, noting the supposed contribution of van de Velde; Wagner 82)

P230

Purchased by the 4th Marquess of Hertford 1865(?)

# William HILTON
## 1786–1839

b. Lincoln, d. London; portrait and history painter, much influenced by Titian and Venetian 16th-century painting; Keeper of the Royal Academy from 1827.

**P633    VENUS IN SEARCH OF CUPID SURPRISES DIANA AT HER BATH**

Canvas 154·9 × 190·5

Almost certainly the painting with this title exhibited at the RA in 1820; Cupid hides amongst the trees on the left.

Purchased by the 4th Marquess of Hertford 1854

P633

# Meindert HOBBEMA
## 1638–1709

b. and d. Amsterdam; assumed the name of Hobbema; pupil of J. van Ruisdael, q.v.; appointed a customs official in 1668 after which his activity as a landscape painter diminished.

**P60   A RUIN ON THE BANK OF A RIVER**

Signed: *M. Hobbema*

Panel 60·0 × 84·5

A favourite motif of Hobbema's, this river was also painted by his master, Ruisdael. (HdG 17)

Purchased by the 4th Marquess of Hertford 1868

P60

**P75   A STORMY LANDSCAPE**

Signed: *M. Hobbema f. 166[3?]*

Canvas 98·7 × 131·1

Cleaned and restored 1975. (HdG 167)

Purchased by the 4th Marquess of Hertford 1845

P75

## P95   A WOODED LANDSCAPE

Signed: *M. Hobbema*

Canvas 76·8 × 110·2

(HdG 168)

Purchased by the 4th Marquess of Hertford 1865

P95

## P99   A WATERMILL

Signed: *M. Hobbema*

Panel 69·2 × 92·1

Painted *c.* 1665. One of Hobbema's favourite scenes; other examples in the Art Institute, Chicago, and the Rijksmuseum, Amsterdam. (HdG 85)

Purchased by the 4th Marquess of Hertford 1850

P99

## P164   THE OUTSKIRTS OF A WOOD

Signed: *M. Hobbema*

Panel 54·9 × 67·9

This picture is visible in Adriaan de Lelie's *Jan Gildmeester Jansz in his house*, dated 1794–95, in the Rijksmuseum, Amsterdam. (HdG 227, 244)

Purchased by Sir Richard Wallace 1872

P164

# Hans HOLBEIN the younger, after
## 1497/8–1543

b. Augsburg, d. London; worked for Henry VIII from 1532, having previously visited London in 1526.

### P547   KING EDWARD VI

Paper on board 72·7 × 54·6

A 19th-century adaptation of the drawing, previously called Holbein, of Edward, Prince of Wales, at Windsor. Edward VI (1537–53) ascended the throne in 1547 but died young from consumption.

Acquired by 1872

P547

### P554   JANE SEYMOUR, THIRD QUEEN OF HENRY VIII

Paper on canvas 72·7 × 54·6

A 19th-century adaptation of the drawing by Holbein at Windsor. Jane Seymour (1509?–37) m. Henry VIII in 1536; she died soon after giving birth to Edward, see P547 above. Her brother Edward was the ancestor of the Marquesses of Hertford, see Corneille de Lyon P352.

Acquired by 1872

P554

# Melchior de HONDECOETER
## 1636–1695

b. Utrecht, d. Amsterdam; pupil of his father and of his uncle, J. B. Weenix, q.v.; worked in the Hague 1659–63, and then at Amsterdam.

**P64    PEACOCKS AND DUCKS**

Signed: *M. d Hondecoeter*

Canvas 210·8 × 176·5

Acquired by 1872

P64

P83

**P83    A COCK AND OTHER BIRDS**

Signed: *M. D. Hondecoeter*

Canvas 107·3 × 127·6

Acquired by the 4th Marquess of Hertford by 1859

# Hendrik HONDIUS (the elder?)
## 1573–1649

b. Duffel, Brabant; engraver of works by Dürer, Holbein and Brueghel; Hendrik Hondius the younger (1597?–1644?), was also an engraver of comparable subjects.

### P771 DEATH AND THE HUNTSMAN

Signed: *1625 Hh fecit*

Sepia with blue washes 15·9 × 9·8

Würzbach attributed this elaborate allegory to the elder Hondius, though the subject is perhaps more typical of the younger's work.

P771

# Pieter de HOOGH
## 1629–after 1684?

b. Rotterdam; pupil of Nicolaes Berchem, q.v., and Jacob Ochtervelt, presumably in Haarlem; working in Delft 1653; moved to Amsterdam by 1663 and remained there until at least 1677.

### P23 A WOMAN PEELING APPLES

Canvas 70·5 × 54·3

Dated *c.* 1663 by Valentiner; a comparable interior appears in the *Mother and Child* in the M.H. de Young Museum, San Francisco. (HdG 33)

Purchased by the 4th Marquess of Hertford 1848

P23

P27

### P27   A BOY BRINGING POMEGRANATES

Signed: *PDH*

Canvas 73·7 × 60·2

Dated *c.* 1662 by Valentiner, and *c.* 1665 by de Groot. (HdG 34)

Purchased by the 4th Marquess of Hertford 1865

# John HOPPNER
## 1758?–1810

b. and d. London; much influenced by Reynolds, q.v.; Principal Painter to the Prince of Wales 1793.

P563

### P563   KING GEORGE IV AS PRINCE OF WALES

Canvas 127·3 × 101·6

George IV (1762–1830), Prince Regent 1811, and King 1820, a frequent companion of the second Marchioness of Hertford between 1811–20; see also Géricault P755 and Lawrence P559. Probably painted *c.* 1792–96; the Prince received P563 from Hoppner's widow in 1810 and he presented it to the future 3rd Marquess of Hertford the same year. A full-length of the Prince in Garter robes by Hoppner was in the collection of the 2nd Marquess of Hertford by 1812; it is now at Ragley Hall.

Purchased by the 4th Marquess of Hertford 1855

# Hubertus van HOVE
## 1814–1865

b. The Hague, d. Antwerp; pupil of his father, Bartolomeus Johannes van Hove; worked in The Hague until 1854, then in Antwerp.

### P736   A DOORWAY AT ANTWERP

Signed: *HVH* and *BJZ* (both in monogram, the second meaning Bartolomeus Johannes Zohn, i.e. son of Bartolomeus Johannes)

Water-colour 15·9 × 11·7

Acquired by 1872

P736

# Jan van HUIJSUM
## 1682–1749

b. and d. Amsterdam; pupil of his father, Justus; worked principally in Amsterdam.

### P149   FLOWERS IN A VASE

Signed: *Jan Van Huijsum fecit 1726*

Panel 80·0 × 60·3

(HdG 58)

Acquired by 1872

P149

P207

## P207 FRUIT AND FLOWERS

Signed: *Jan Van Huijsum fecit*

Panel 80·6 × 60·3

Two related drawings by van Huijsum are in the Metropolitan Museum, New York, and in the Schlossmuseum, Weimar. A copy in oils by Jan van Os (1744–1808) is in the Fitzwilliam Museum, Cambridge. (HdG 57)

Acquired by 1872

# Jean-Auguste-Dominique INGRES
## 1780–1867

b. Montauban, d. Paris; pupil of David; worked in Rome and Florence 1806–24, deeply influenced by Raphael; apart from a second visit to Rome 1834–41, worked in Paris for the rest of his life.

P767

## P767 HOPE AND CHARITY after Raphael

Signed: *Ingres à son ami Calamatta*

Pencil 35·6 × 36·2 (four drawings cut out and laid down)

The two putti and the lower roundel (*Charity*) come from the same Raphael predella panel, and the upper roundel (*Hope*) from part of another (both in the Vatican Museum, originally with the Borghese *Entombment*). Luigi Calamatta (1802–69), an Italian engraver, came to Paris 1822 and made several plates after Ingres.

# Louis-Gabriel-Eugène ISABEY
## 1803–1886

b. Paris, d. Montevrain; son of miniaturist J-B. Isabey; painter of romantic genre scenes and marine subjects; see also Scheffer P298.

**P271   COURT RECEPTION AT A CHATEAU**

Signed: *E. Isabey 1851*

Canvas 64·8 × 91·1

Acquired by 1872

P271

**P335   THE YOUNG MOTHER**

Signed: *E. Isabey 52*

Canvas 41·9 × 29·8

Another version recorded entitled *La famille du peintre*.

Acquired by 1872

P335

**P360   A PROMENADE BY THE SEA**

Signed: *E. Isabey 46*

Canvas 50·8 × 68·6

Acquired by 1872

P360

**P579   BOATS ON THE SHORE AT CALAIS**

Signed: *E. Isabey 1851*

Canvas 61·9 × 91·4

Purchased by the 4th Marquess of Hertford 1863

P579

# ITALIAN SCHOOL
18th century

**P493 VIEW OF THE GRAND HARBOUR AND CITY OF VALETTA, MALTA**

Canvas 106·7 × 207·6

Apparently based on an engraving by P. N. Milcent (fl. 1730–40). Tentatively attributed by Constable to Giuseppe Guerra (d. 1761). (Constable, *Canaletto*, 518)

Acquired by 1872

P493

# Claude (Claudius) JACQUAND
1804–1878

b. Lyons, d. Paris; studied in Lyons; portrait, decorative and genre painter.

P648

**P648   SOLDIERS GAMBLING**

Signed: *Claudius Jacquand 1856*

Canvas 53·9 × 70·5

The costumes appear to be of the early 17th century.

Acquired by 1872

# Karel du JARDIN
## 1621/22?–1678

b. probably Amsterdam, d. Venice; pupil of Berchem, q.v. in The Hague, and influenced by Paulus Potter, q.v.; studied and worked in Italy in the 1640s and from 1675, in Amsterdam 1650–55 and 1659–75, and The Hague 1655–59.

### P222   THE SMITHY

Signed: *K. du Jardin fec. 1658*

Canvas 48·3 × 52·4

(HdG 337)

Purchased by the 4th Marquess of Hertford 1846

P222

### P241   GENTLEMAN IN A RED CLOAK

Copper 31·1 × 23·8

An attribution to Michael Sweerts (1624–64) and the identification of the sitter as the poet Isaac van de Merwede, have been tentatively proposed. (HdG 396)

Purchased by the 4th Marquess of Hertford 1848

P241

### P641   THE    STROLLING    BALLAD-SINGERS

Panel 23·5 diameter

Probably from du Jardin's first Roman period, in the 1640s. (HdG 342)

Purchased by the 4th Marquess of Hertford 1848

P641

# Tony JOHANNOT
## 1803–1852

b. Offenbach, d. Paris; one of three brothers, all artists; illustrator and engraver.

P693

**P693   MINNA AND BRENDA**

Signed: *Tony Johannot*

Water-colour 42·5 × 34·0

The subject is taken from Scott's *The Pirate* 1821.

Acquired by 1872

P739

**P739   A YOUNG GIRL ASLEEP**

Signed: *Tony Johannot*

Water-colour 10·8 × 7·9

The old mount is inscribed 'The Fair Sleeper'.

Acquired by 1872

# Jacques (Jacob) JORDAENS
## 1593–1678

b. and d. Antwerp; pupil of Adam van Noort and, later, assistant of Rubens, q.v., who greatly influenced him; on Rubens's death, he became the 'prime painter' of Antwerp.

### P120   THE RICHES OF AUTUMN

Canvas 201·3 × 229·9

The subject appears to derive from Ripa's emblem of *Abondanza* (in his *Iconologia* of 1593) with the additional figures of nymphs and satyrs. Probably painted 1625–28; the fruit, vegetables and foliage are attributed to F. Snijders, q.v. Other versions of this subject, differing in the central group, are in the Musée des Beaux-Arts and a private collection, Brussels.

Purchased by Sir Richard Wallace 1872(?)

P120

## Niclas LAFRENSEN (Lavreince)
### 1737–1807

b. and d. Stockholm; worked in Paris *c.* 1760–69 and 1774–91; in Stockholm appointed court miniaturist 1770 and Painter to the King 1773. See also *Catalogue of Miniatures*.

### P772   CONVERSATION GALANTE

Ink and wash 17·1 × 12·1

P772

# Eugène (Louis) LAMI
## 1800–1890

b. and d. Paris; pupil of H. Vernet, q.v., and Bonington, q.v.; in England 1826–27 and 1848–52; architectural adviser to Baron James de Rothschild; history painter in oil and water-colour.

P653

**P653  L'ESCALIER DES AMBASSADEURS, VERSAILLES**

Signed: *E.L.* and *E.L. 1866*

Water-colour 32·1 × 50·5

This noble staircase, designed by Le Vau, was begun in 1671 and decorated by Le Brun; it was demolished in 1752. Lami probably used Surugue's engraving as his source.

Acquired by 1872

P663

**P663  A SUPPER WITH THE REGENT**

Signed: EUGENE LAMI 1854

Water-colour 38·4 × 66·0

Philippe, duc d'Orléans (1674–1723), Regent 1715–23 during the minority of Louis XV, relaxed the austerity which had prevailed at Court during the final years of Louis XIV.

Acquired by 1872

P702

**P702  THE COURT OF LOUIS XIV IN FLANDERS**

Signed: *E.L.*

Water-colour 19·1 × 34·3

Acquired by 1872

P710

**P710  THE ROYAL PROCESSION, OPENING OF PARLIAMENT, 1855**

Signed: EUG. LAMI 1855

Water-colour 15·2 × 31·8

Commissioned by Anatole Demidoff, duc de San-Donato, who had m. Mathilde, d. of Jérôme Bonaparte; 1855 was the year of the successful World Fair in Paris and of the exchange of state visits between Queen Victoria and Napoleon III.

Purchased by the 4th Marquess of Hertford 1870

## P723  BRITISH HORSE ARTILLERY AT A REVIEW

Signed: EUG. LAMI

Water-colour 29·5 × 49·2

Sold in 1870 as *Revue du régiment du Royal Horse Artillery et du 17e Lancers à Woolwich, 14 Mai 1851*

Purchased by the 4th Marquess of Hertford 1870

P723

# Nicolas LANCRET
## 1690–1743

b. and d. Paris; studied at the Académie and with Claude Gillot; he was *agréé* by the Académie in 1718 (see P422), and, following the death of Watteau in 1721, became the leading painter of *fêtes galantes*.

## P378  A GIRL IN A KITCHEN

Panel 29·8 × 25·7

Probably a late work. The girl has been painted over another indecipherable figure and a dog which formed part of the original kitchen interior, evidently by another hand and attributed to Willem Kalf (1622–93). Other instances of Lancret thus embellishing a 17th-century Dutch kitchen scene are recorded; two are in the Hermitage Museum, Leningrad.

Purchased by the 4th Marquess of Hertford 1859

P378

## P393  MADEMOISELLE CAMARGO DANCING

Canvas 43·2 × 55·2

Marie de Camargo (1710–41), dancer and courtesan, was born in Brussels and made her debut on the Paris stage in 1726. Her celebrated rival, Mlle. Salle, was the subject of a pendant to P393. Painted before August 1730; engraved by L. Cars 1731. Three other versions are recorded, in Nantes, Leningrad and Washington.

Purchased by Sir Richard Wallace 1872

P393

P401

## P401 AN ITALIAN COMEDY SCENE

Canvas 29·8 × 36·8

Polichinelle struts while Harlequin makes advances to Columbine. A pendant to *Le joueur de flûte* which is now untraced.

Acquired by 1872

P408

## P408 GIRLS BATHING

Canvas 25·4 × 34·3

A copy in miniature is in The Wallace Collection, M128.

Purchased by the 4th Marquess of Hertford 1865

P409

## P409 A TALE FROM LA FONTAINE

Copper 27·9 × 35·6

From La Fontaine, *Contes* iii, 14; Manto, a fairy changed into a spaniel who can produce jewels and money, abets Atis, lover of Argie, whose husband is absent. One of twelve illustrations to La Fontaine by Lancret. Engraved by N. Larmessin.

Purchased by the 4th Marquess of Hertford 1857

P422

## P422 CONVERSATION GALANTE

Canvas 73·7 × 58·4

Apparently the picture engraved by Le Bas 1743 as Lancret's *morceau de réception* for the Académie, presented in 1719. The engraving agrees exactly with P422 but the measurements then given for the original painting (*c.* 69 × 35) differ (but present an impossible proportion and are clearly mistaken).

## P436 THE BIRD-CATCHERS

Copper 33·0 × 41·3

Pendant to a *Danse champêtre*, now untraced. A similar subject exhibited by Lancret at the Salon of 1738 as *Spring* from a set of the seasons painted for the château de La Muette.

Acquired by the 4th Marquess of Hertford by 1859

P436

## P448 FÊTE IN A WOOD

Canvas 65·1 × 92·1

An early work, strongly influenced by Watteau; acquired as a work by Pater, q.v.

Acquired by 1872

P448

## P450 LA BELLE GRECQUE

Canvas 70·2 × 56·2

A version engraved by Schmidt 1736; pendant to *Le Turc amoureux*. Several versions of each subject are recorded, though none exactly corresponds to the engraving.

Acquired by 1872

P450

## P465 ITALIAN COMEDIANS BY A FOUNTAIN

Canvas 92·4 × 85·1

A fine, early work, cf. P422 above. Cleaned and restored 1977. A pentimento in the background shows that there was originally an architectural setting (cf. Watteau's *Le bal champêtre* at Dulwich).

Purchased by the 4th Marquess of Hertford 1853

P465

P478

### P478 PASTORAL REVELS

Cooper 33·7 × 41·3

Inscribed, verso, *peint par Lancret 1738*. The painting combines elements from several Lancret compositions.

Acquired by the 4th Marquess of Hertford by 1859

## Charles LANDELLE
### 1821–1908

b. Laval, d. Chennevières-sur-Marne; pupil of Delaroche, q.v., and Scheffer, q.v.; decorative and historical painter whose oriental subjects became popular.

P278

### P278 AN ARMENIAN WOMAN

Signed: CH. LANDELLE 1866

Canvas 130·5 × 81·9

Purchased by the 4th Marquess of Hertford 1868

## Edwin Henry LANDSEER
### 1802–1873

b. and d. London; pupil of his father, John, and the RA schools; portrait and animal painter, knighted in 1850.

P257

### P257 LOOKING FOR CRUMBS FROM THE RICH MAN'S TABLE

Canvas 63·5 × 76·2

Commissioned by Elkanah Bicknell and exhibited at the RA in 1859.

Purchased by the 4th Marquess of Hertford 1863

## P373    A HIGHLAND SCENE

Panel 28·9 × 43·2

Probably painted *c.* 1850.

Purchased by the 4th Marquess of Hertford 1859

P373

## P376    THE ARAB TENT

Canvas 153·7 × 226·1

Exhibited at the RA in 1866 and bought by the Prince of Wales.

Purchased from the Prince by Sir Richard Wallace after 1874

P376

## P589    MISS NELLIE POWER

Signed: EHL (monogram)

Chalks 62·9 × 47·3

Niece of the Countess of Blessington (see Lawrence P558) with whom she lived from *c.* 1832, together with her older sister, Marguerite Power (*c.* 1815–67); believed to have become a nun and to have died in 1872.

Purchased by the 4th Marquess of Hertford 1849

P589

# Thomas LAWRENCE
## 1769–1830

b. Bristol, d. London; studied at the RA schools, a precocious youth who became a brilliant portrait painter; knighted in 1815.

P39

### P39  MISS SALLY SIDDONS

Canvas 76·5 × 63·8

Sally Siddons (1775–1803), one of the celebrated Sarah Siddons's two daughters; Lawrence reputedly flirted with both of them. Painted *c.* 1795–1800. Lawrence painted a second portrait of Sally, a three-quarter length sold in New York 1933.

Purchased by the 4th Marquess of Hertford 1863(?)

P41

### P41  A LADY

Canvas 76·5 × 64·1

Painted in the 1790s. Published in 1905 as a work by Hoppner but there is now little doubt concerning an attribution to the young Lawrence.

Purchased by the 4th Marquess of Hertford 1855(?)

## P558    THE COUNTESS OF BLESSINGTON

Canvas 91·4 × 71·8

Marguerite Power (1789–1849), authoress and a famous beauty, m. 1st in 1807 Captain Farmer (d. 1817) and, 2nd in 1818 Charles, 1st Earl of Blessington (d. 1829); her constant companion from the mid-1820s was the artist and dandy, Alfred, Count D'Orsay (1801–52). Exhibited at the RA in 1822 when the sight of the sitter viewing her portrait prompted the comment, 'I have seen no other so striking instance of the inferiority of art to nature' (P. G. Patmore). For a copy in miniature, see *Catalogue of Miniatures*, M27.

Purchased by the 4th Marquess of Hertford 1849

P558

## P559    KING GEORGE IV

Canvas 269·9 × 178·4

George IV (1762–1830), Prince Regent 1811–20, and King 1820–30; see also Géricault P755 and Hoppner P563. Painted in 1822 for the Marchioness Conyngham, Lawrence considered this his most successful likeness of the King; it was engraved four times before 1841, and many versions are recorded. The Order of the Golden Fleece of Austria which the King is wearing was a Catholic honour, awarded to George IV by special Papal dispensation in 1815.

Purchased by Sir Richard Wallace 1883

P559

# Élizabeth-Louise Vigée-LEBRUN
## 1755–1842

b. and d. Paris; daughter of a minor painter, pupil of Biard; *agréée* by the Académie 1783 she became a successful portrait painter, and a favourite of Marie-Antoinette; travelled in Europe and Russia *c.* 1792–1805; for a portrait of her in miniature, see *Catalogue of Miniatures*, M101.

P449

### P449   LE COMTE D'ESPAGNAC

Canvas 64·8 × 54·3

The sitter was Joseph-François-Pierre-Guillaume de Sahuget Damazit d'Espagnac (b. 1776). Painted in 1786 and exhibited in the Salon of 1787 as *M. le baron d'Espagnac, le fils*.

Purchased by the 4th Marquess of Hertford 1868

P457

### P457   MADAME PERREGAUX

Signed: *Louise Vigée Le Brun f. 1789*

Panel 99·7 × 78·4

Adelaïde de Prael (1758–94) m. J-F. Perregaux, a Swiss banker, in 1779. Exhibited at the Salon in 1791 as *Une jeune dame Espagnole* (from her black dress, *à l'espagnole*).

Purchased by the 4th Marquess of Hertford 1862(?)

# François LEMOYNE
## 1688–1737

b. and d. Paris; pupil of Galloche, *agrée* by the Académie 1718; a decorative painter of considerable ability employed by the King at Versailles; *premier peintre du roi* 1736; for a short period the master of Boucher, q.v.

### P392 TIME REVEALING TRUTH

Canvas 182·9 × 148·6

The figure of Time with his sickle shows Truth to another, recumbent, figure. Painted in 1737, this was Lemoyne's last work; he committed suicide within hours of its completion. A copy in Beauvais tapestry is in the Musée Bargoin, Clermont-Ferrand.

Purchased by the 4th Marquess of Hertford 1851(?)

P392

### P417   PERSEUS AND ANDROMEDA

Signed: *f. Le Moyne, 1723*

Canvas 184·2 × 151·4

The subject is taken from Ovid, *Metamorphoses* iv; see Titian P11. Exhibited in the Salon of 1725 with *Hercules and Omphale* (184 × 149, Louvre) as its pendant. The composition derives, apparently, from the *Perseus and Andromeda* attributed to Veronese (Musée des Beaux-Arts, Rennes); it became well-known and appeared in the 18th century as a Fürstenberg porcelain group, on a Vincennes wine-cooler, and on a Meissen snuff-box; it was also copied by Angelica Kauffman.

Purchased by the 4th Marquess of Hertford 1851(?)

P417

## Nicolas-Bernard LÉPICIÉ
### 1735–1784

b. and d. Paris; pupil of Carle van Loo, q.v., *agréé* by the Académie 1769, becoming Professor and *premier peintre du roi*; history and genre painter.

### P464    A MOTHER FEEDING HER CHILD

Signed: *Lépicié*

Panel 15·2 × 11·1

A larger version (45 × 37) is signed and dated 1774 (London art market 1963). The composition formed part of the *Ménage de bonnes gens* (engraved by Longueil in 1788). Probably pendant to P466 below.

Purchased by the 4th Marquess of Hertford 1868(?)

P464

### P466    THE READING LESSON

Signed: *Lépicié*

Panel 15·2 × 11·1

Study for the left hand group in *La famille du menuisier* which was exhibited in the Salon of 1775 (London art market 1978). Probably pendant to P464 above.

Purchased by the 4th Marquess of Hertford 1868(?)

P466

## Hendrik Jan August, Baron LEYS
### 1815–1869

b. and d. Antwerp; a celebrated history painter, initially influenced by 17th-century Dutch artists such as Metsu and de Hoogh (q.v.), and later by 16th-century German and Netherlandish art.

### P275    FRANS FLORIS GOING TO A PAINTERS' FEAST

Signed: *H. Leys f$^t$ 1853*

Canvas 66·0 × 89·9

Frans Floris (1520–70), like Leys an Antwerp painter, attending a St Luke's Day celebration (held annually by the painters' Guilds, of whom St Luke was the patron Saint).

Purchased by the 4th Marquess of Hertford 1863

P275

P570

**P570   SOLDIERS PLAYING CARDS**

Signed: *H. Leys 1849*

Panel 36·8 × 45·1

Acquired by 1872

# Charles-André (Carle) van LOO
## 1705–1765

b. Nice, d. Paris; pupil of his brother J-B. van Loo and of Benedetto Luti at Rome; visited Italy 1716–20 and 1728–34 (with Boucher, q.v., and L-M. van Loo, q.v.); portrait, history and decorative painter; *premier peintre du roi* 1762, Director of the Académie 1763. (M-C. Sahut, *Carle Vanloo*, Nice, 1977).

P451

**P451   THE GRAND TURK GIVING A CONCERT TO HIS MISTRESS**

Signed: *Carle Van Loo 1737*

Canvas 74·0 × 92·1

Exhibited at the Salon 1737 with its pendant, *The Grand Turk having his Mistress painted* (Museum of Fine Arts, Richmond, Virginia). The model for the singer in P451 was Christina Somis (1704–85) who m. the artist in 1733 at Turin. Several copies, or versions, are recorded, including a Sèvres plaque. (Sahut 52) Purchased by Sir Richard Wallace 1867

## Louis-Michel van LOO
### 1707–1771

b. Toulon, d. Paris; nephew of Carle, q.v., and son of J-B. van Loo; in Italy 1728–34 (with Boucher, q.v. and Carle van Loo); portrait painter, appointed painter to the Spanish Bourbon court 1737–52; continued to practise successfully on his return to Paris.

### P477    LOUIS XV IN ROBES OF STATE

Canvas 137·5 × 105·4

Louis XV (1710–74) acceded in 1715; during his minority, until 1723, France was ruled by the Régent, the duc d'Orléans (see Lami P663). P477 is a reduced version of a portrait painted in 1761, now unidentified; many versions are recorded, copies being given by the King to his ministers and ambassadors; an example at Woburn is sd 1762.
Purchased by the 4th Marquess of Hertford 1855

P477

## Bernardino LUINI
### active 1512    d. 1532

Active in and around Milan; greatly influenced by Leonardo da Vinci in his mature works.

### P8    THE VIRGIN AND CHILD

Panel 73·7 × 54·0
Acquired by 1872

P8

P10

### P10 THE VIRGIN OF THE COLUMBINE

Panel 74·9 × 57·2

The columbine was used to symbolise the Holy Ghost (its shape being like a white dove). The influence of Leonardo da Vinci is apparent in the soft modelling and colour. Versions of this composition are at Apsley House; the Hermitage, Leningrad, and in private collections in Italy, America and England.

Purchased by the 4th Marquess of Hertford 1865

P526

### P526 THE YOUNG BACCHUS

Fresco 50·5 × 65·7 transferred to canvas

With P537 below, part of a decorative scheme executed *c*. 1520–23 for the Villa Pelucca, near Monza; 34 fragments survive from four rooms (the majority now in the Brera, Milan). P526 and P537 were from the same room and an inscription on the verso of P526 records the transfer of this fragment on to canvas in June 1824.

P537

### P537 HEAD OF A GIRL

Fresco 49·2 × 36·5 transferred to panel

See P526 above; P537 was part of a group of girls at play.

## Nicolaes MAES
### 1632–1693

b. Dordrecht, d. Amsterdam; pupil of Rembrandt; worked in Dordrecht 1653–73, then in Amsterdam; early religious subjects succeeded by domestic genre in the 1650s, and by portraiture after 1660.

## P224   THE LISTENING MAID

Signed: *N. Maes 1656*

Canvas 86·4 × 72·1

The pot in the maid's hand reappears, for example, in the Maes in the National Gallery, no. 159, which is dated 1655. Other versions of this subject are in the Royal Collection, the Six collection, Amsterdam, and at Apsley House. (HdG 124)

Acquired by 1872

P224

## P239   HOUSEWIFE AT WORK

Signed: *N. Maes*

Panel 74·9 × 60·3

Painted *c.* 1656. (HdG 60)

Acquired between 1866 and 1872

P239

# Carlo MARATTI, attributed to
## 1625–1713

b. Camerano, d. Rome; pupil of Sacchi and much influenced by Guido Reni and the Carracci; painted portraits and history subjects, but particularly favoured for his religious pieces.

### P774   THE VIRGIN OF MERCY

Red chalk 24·1 × 16·8

Inscribed below: *ma este donné par le Prince Dom Livio / Carlo Marato / 58*, in a hand identified as that of Pierre Crozat (1665–1740) who was given some one hundred drawings by the Prince Livio Odescalchi (d. 1713) for his part in negotiating the sale of Queen Christina of Sweden's collection to Philippe, duc d.Orléans, the Regent of France. See also Polidoro, P775.

P774

# Prosper MARILHAT
## 1811–1847

b. Vertaizon (Puy-de-Dôme), d. Paris; pupil of Roqueplan, q.v.; travelled in the east 1831–33 and won the sobriquet *le Meissonier de l'Afrique*.

**P293   BENISOEF ON THE NILE**
Signed: P. MARILHAT
Panel 30·8 × 45·4
Acquired by 1872

P293

**P317   PALM TREES**
Canvas 34·3 × 23·5
Acquired by 1872

P317

**P334   THE ERECHTHEUM, ATHENS**
Signed: P. MARILHAT 1841
Canvas 74·3 × 92·7
Possibly shown in the Salon of 1841.
Acquired by 1872

P334

**P356   A SCENE ON THE NILE**
Canvas 45·1 × 73·7
Acquired by 1872

P356

# Jean Louis de MARNE
## 1752–1829

b. Brussels, d. Paris; pupil of Briard; history and landscape painter; worked for
a time at the Sèvres porcelain factory.

### P462   WOMEN AND SOLDIERS
### REVELLING

Canvas 49·2 × 56·8
Acquired by 1859

P462

### P469   THE ELIXIR

Canvas 50·5 × 61·3
Acquired by 1859

P469

# MASTER of the MAGDALEN LEGEND, after
## active late 15th early 16th century

Named after a dispersed triptych of *c.* 1515–20; probably active in Brussels;
attributed works date from 1483 to 1527.

### P548   THE VIRGIN AND CHILD

Panel 24·8 × 17·8

Based on the central motif of the Master's
*Virgin with a Pink* (from a triptych in the Musée
Mayer van den Bergh, Antwerp).

P548

# Marie-Françoise-Constance La Martinière MAYER
## 1778–1821

b. and d. Paris; pupil of Suvée, Greuze, q.v., and Prud'hon, q.v., whose mistress she became and who dominated her art, see Prud'hon, P313.

### P348 THE SLEEP OF VENUS AND CUPID

Canvas 97·5 × 145·7

Commissioned by the Empress Joséphine and exhibited in the Salon of 1806. The work seems to have been designed by Prud'hon by whom preparatory drawings and two oil sketches exist. Pendant to *Le flambeau de Vénus* shown in the Salon of 1808.

Acquired by 1872

P348

# Jean-Louis-Ernest MEISSONIER
## 1815–1891

b. Lyon, d. Paris; pupil of Pothier and Cogniet, q.v.; his earlier works, small historical genre pieces, achieved considerable popularity and brought official honours; his later historical and allegorical pictures were less well received; he was a friend of (Sir) Richard Wallace.

P287

### P287 A SENTINEL: TIME OF LOUIS XIII

Signed: *EM 1851*

Panel 26·7 × 16·5

Acquired by 1872

## P289    HALT AT AN INN

Signed: *EMeissonier* and *EM*

Panel    19·7 × 25·1    (enlarged    from    *c.*
18·7 × 24·5)

Engraved in 1863 without the additions top
and right; sold in 1865 in present form.
Painted *c.* 1862.

Purchased by the 4th Marquess of Hertford
1865

P289

## P290    NAPOLEON I AND HIS STAFF

Signed: *EMeissonier 1868*

Panel 15·2 × 18·1

Napoleon wears the uniform of the Chasseurs
and is followed by his generals and an
Egyptian follower (extreme left) added, it was
said, at the express wish of Lord Hertford.

Purchased by the 4th Marquess of Hertford
1870(?)

P290

## P291    A CAVALIER: TIME OF LOUIS XIII

Signed: *EMeissonier 1861*

Panel 24·1 × 18·4

Purchased by the 4th Marquess of Hertford
1864

P291

## P297    THE PROPHET ISAIAH

Signed: *EM*

Panel 35·2 × 23·8

Exhibited in the Salon of 1840 and engraved
by Cousin for an edition of Bossuet's *Discours*
published in 1841. Previously listed as *St John
in Patmos*.

Acquired by 1872

P297

P325

**P325   AN   ARTIST   SHOWING   HIS WORK**

Signed: *EM*

Panel 38·7 × 29·8

Exhibited in the Salon of 1850–51. On the wall behind hangs Meissonier's *The Smoker*.

Acquired by 1872

P326

**P326   "À   L'OMBRE   DES   BOSQUETS CHANTE UN JEUNE POÈTE"**

Panel 18·4 × 21·6

Exhibited in the Salon of 1853. The title acknowledges a poem by Charles Regnault written in May 1850 in praise of this picture and dedicated to the artist.

Acquired by 1872

P327

**P327   THE HIRED ASSASSINS**

Signed: *EMeissonier 1852*

Panel 38·1 × 28·9

Exhibited in the Salon of 1852.

Purchased by the 4th Marquess of Hertford 1865

P328

**P328   THE ROADSIDE INN**

Signed: *EMeissonier Septembre 1865*

Panel 24·4 × 19·7

Purchased by the 4th Marquess of Hertford 1870

### P329   COLONEL FÉLIX MASSUE

Signed: *Au Colonel Félix Massue, souvenir affec-*
*tueux. EMeissonier 1867*

Panel 13·0 × 11·1

P329

### P330   THE LOST GAME

Signed: *EMeissonier 1858*

Panel 21·6 × 27·0

Pendant to *The Winning Game* (private collection, U.S.A.).

Acquired by 1872

P330

### P331   A CAVALIER: TIME OF LOUIS XIV

Signed: *EM 1856*

Panel 14·0 × 9·5

Acquired by 1872

P331

### P332   A MUSKETEER: TIME OF LOUIS XIII

Signed: *EMeissonier 1856*

Panel 28·3 × 18·1

Acquired by 1872

P332

P337

### P337 POLICHINELLE

Signed: *EM 1860*

Panel 56·2 × 36·8

Originally painted on a door panel for Mme. Sabatier, whose circle included Meissonier, Baudelaire and Richard Wallace; P337 was in her sale in 1861.

P369

### P369 DUTCH BURGHERS

Signed: *EMeissonier*

Panel 19·1 × 24·8

A very early work, probably painted *c.* 1834. Acquired by Sir Richard Wallace after 1872

P371

### P371 THE GUARD ROOM

Signed: *EMeissonier 1857*

Panel 16·2 × 20·0

Acquired by 1872

# Hans MEMLINC
## active 1465 died 1494

b. near Frankfurt, d. Bruges; influenced by Roger van der Weyden and Dieric Bouts (K. B. Mcfarlane, *Hans Memling*, Oxford, 1971).

## P528    THE ARCHANGEL MICHAEL

Panel 36·5 × 16·2

The dark clouds suggest the passage in *Revelation* xii, 7–9, in which Michael fights against the Devil in the war of heaven. Evidently a fragment, P528 has been tentatively identified with one of the shutters of a triptych painted for Marguerite of Austria listed in 1524 (the centre panel was a Pietà by Roger van der Weyden). A border, approximately 3·8 wide, has been repainted all round (covering the clouds, wing tips and elbows). (Mcfarlane, p. 35)

P528

# Francisco MENESES Osorio, attributed to
## 1630?–1705?

b. and d. Seville; pupil of Murillo whose work he imitated; worked in Vallodolid, Seville and Madrid.

## P7    THE ASSUMPTION OF THE VIRGIN

Canvas 168·6 × 110·8

Previously called 'School of Murillo'; a drawing for the Virgin in the Witt collection, inscribed *Meneses*, suggests the current attribution, first proposed in 1956.

Purchased by the 4th Marquess of Hertford 1848

P7

# Hughes MERLE
## 1823–1881

b. Saint-Marcellin, d. Paris; pupil of Cogniet, q.v., painter of popular romantic and sentimental genre scenes.

### P597    READING THE BIBLE

Signed: *H. Merle*

Canvas 21·6 × 27·3

Probably exhibited in the Salon of 1872.

P597


# Gabriel METSU
## 1629–1667

b. Leiden, d. Amsterdam; probably a pupil of Dou, q.v., working in Leiden until the 1650s; settled in Amsterdam 1657. (Franklin W. Robinson, *Gabriel Metsu*, New York, 1974)

### P206    A LADY AT HER MIRROR

Signed: *G. Metsu*

Panel 19·1 × 16·5

Probably painted in the late 1650s. (Robinson, p. 50, fig. 123; HdG 87)

Acquired by 1872

P206

### P234    AN OLD WOMAN SELLING FISH

Signed: *G. Metsu* and *M*

Panel 48·6 × 39·1

Probably painted in the late 1650s, reflecting the influence of Dou. (Robinson, p. 43, fig. 88; HdG 33)

Acquired by the 4th Marquess of Hertford by 1857

P234

## P240   THE LETTER-WRITER SURPRISED

Signed: *Gabriel Metsu*

Panel 46·4 × 38·7

Probably painted in the early 1660s; the bust of the girl which appears in the background of P240 also appears in Metsu's *Portrait of the Artist* (H.M. The Queen), *A Woman drawing* (National Gallery, no. 5225), and *An Artist painting a Woman playing a 'cello* (London art market 1949). (Robinson, p. 39, fig. 74; HdG 186)

Purchased by the 4th Marquess of Hertford 1867

P240

## P242   AN OLD WOMAN ASLEEP

Signed: *G. Metsu*

Canvas 42·2 × 35·6

Probably painted in the late 1650s, reflecting the influence of Dou. (Robinson, p. 43, fig. 91; HdG 122)

Purchased by the 4th Marquess of Hertford 1848

P242

## P251   THE SLEEPING SPORTSMAN

Signed: *G. Metsu*

Canvas 42·2 × 37·1

Probably painted in the late 1650s, and possibly the sportsman is Metsu himself. (Robinson, p. 30, fig. 36; HdG 229)

P251

## Steven van der MEULEN, attributed to
### active 1543–1568

Trained in Antwerp under W. van Cleve 1543; member of the Antwerp Guild 1552; a London resident in 1560, becoming a successful Court painter in the 1560s.

P534

**P534  ROBERT DUDLEY, EARL OF LEICESTER**

Inscribed: *Aetatis 28 156 . . .*

Panel 93·3 × 71·8

Robert Dudley (1532?–88), KG 1559, cr. Earl of Leicester 1564; an unscrupulous and successful courtier. P534 is a contemporary version of a portrait pattern of c. 1565 now attributed to van der Meulen; two other variants exist.

In the collection of the 3rd Marquess of Hertford

## Michiel van MIEREVELD
### 1567–1641

b. and d. Delft; studied with W. Willemsz and Augustyn at Delft and A. van Blocklandt at Utrecht; Court painter to the House of Orange at The Hague.

P66

**P66  A DUTCH LADY**

Inscribed: *AEtatis 2[4?] A° 1628*

Panel 67·3 × 55·9

Acquired by 1872

# Frans van MIERIS the elder
## 1635–1681

b. and d. Leiden; pupil of G. Dou, q.v.

**P639   VENUS WITH CUPID AND TWO AMORINI**

Signed: *F. van Mieris A° 1665*

Panel 14·3 × 17·1

(HdG 22)

Acquired by 1872

P639

# Jan van MIERIS
## 1660–1690

b. Leiden, d. Rome; son of Frans the elder, q.v., and elder brother of Willem, q.v.; pupil of his father and G. de Lairesse; worked in Florence and Rome.

**P176   LADY AND CAVALIER**

Signed: *J.V. Mieris f.*

Panel 28·9 × 21·9

The subject was described in 1798 (Tronchin collection sale catalogue) as '*Mieris . . . regarde amoureusement sa femme*'; by 1801 a later edition had '*L'artiste . . . regarde une femme*'. A picture of *Apollo and Daphne* hangs on the wall behind.

Acquired by 1872

P176

# Willem van MIERIS
## 1662–1747

b. and d. Leiden; pupil and imitator of his father Frans the elder, q.v.; younger brother of Jan, q.v.

**P155   THE LUTE-PLAYER**

Signed: *W. Van Mieris Fc! 1711*

Panel 50·2 × 40·3

Grisaille figures of Venus and Hercules appear on the back wall. (HdG 291)

Acquired by 1872

P155

P163

**P163    ANTONY AND CLEOPATRA**

Signed: *W. Van Mieris Fc.! 1691*

Panel 48·3 × 37·1

Exhibited in 1872 as *Joseph and Potiphar's Wife.* (HdG 118)

Purchased by the 4th Marquess of Hertford 1849

P178

**P178    A BOY WITH A DRUM**

Signed: *W. Van Mieris Fc.ᵗ Anº 1702*

Panel 34·0 × 27·9

The children (like the putti in the bas-relief below) play at the occupations of maturity. (HdG 334)

Purchased by the 4th Marquess of Hertford 1843

P179

**P179    PARIS AND OENONE**

Signed: *W. Van Mieris Fc.ᵗ Anº 1698*

Canvas 14·6 × 20·3

The subject is taken from Ovid, *Heroides*, v; Paris has carved *Oenone Beminni.* . (i.e. Oenone Love) in the bark of the tree. Probably the pendant to P181. (HdG 88)

Acquired by 1872

P181

**P181    VENUS WITH THE APPLE AND THE SLEEPING CUPID**

Signed: *W. Van Mieris Fᶜᵗ Anº 1698*

Canvas 14·6 × 20·3

The apple refers to the judgement of Paris (see Boucher P444). Probably the pendant to P179. (HdG 104)

Acquired by 1872

## P188   NYMPH AND SATYR

Signed: *W. Van Mieris Fc Anno 170[0 or 9]*

Copper 27·6 × 22·8

In the 18th century P188 was in the Orléans collection as by F. van Mieris the elder. (HdG 82)

Purchased by the 3rd Marquess of Hertford 1818

P188

## P220   THE GREENGROCER

Signed: *W. Van Mieris Fc<sup>t</sup> Anno 1731*

Panel 40·3 × 33·7

(HdG 187)

Purchased by the 4th Marquess of Hertford 1860

P220

# MILANESE SCHOOL
### early 16th century

## P544   HEAD OF A YOUNG SAINT

Plaster 28·6 × 23·5 made up from 23·5 × 17·0

Possibly another fragment from the Pelucca frescoes, see Luini P526, but the damaged condition and small size makes identification difficult.

P544

# Lizinka Aimée Zoe Rue, Mme. de MIRBEL
## 1796–1849

b. Cherbourg, d. Paris; pupil of the miniaturist Augustin, named *peintre en miniatures de la Chambre de sa Majesté* 1818. See also *Catalogue of Miniatures*.

P763

### P763  J. FENIMORE COOPER

Water-colour 14·0 × 9·5

James Fenimore Cooper (1789–1851) the American novelist, best known for *The Last of the Mohicans* published in 1826, the date of P763 which was drawn in Paris in November with P764 below.

Purchased by Sir Richard Wallace 1872

P764

### P764  SIR WALTER SCOTT

Water-colour 14·0 × 9·5

Sir Walter Scott (1771–1832), the famous Scottish novelist, recorded in his *Journal* sitting to Mme Mirbel in November 1826, when Fenimore Cooper was also present; see P763 above.

Purchased by Sir Richard Wallace 1872

# George MORLAND
## 1763–1804

b. and d. London; pupil of his father, H. R. Morland; painter of rustic and peasant genre scenes, some of which, like P574 below, reflected the influence of contemporary French genre painters such as Greuze and Boilly, q.v.

P574

### P574  A VISIT TO THE BOARDING SCHOOL

Signed: *G. Morland*

Canvas 64·1 × 75·6

Engraved by W. Ward in 1789 as a pendant to *A Visit to the Child at Nurse*, engraved the previous year.

Purchased by Sir Richard Wallace 1873

# Andrew MORTON
## 1802–1845

b. Newcastle-on-Tyne, d. London; portrait painter, studied at the RA schools.

**P632    THE DUKE OF WELLINGTON WITH COL. GURWOOD AT APSLEY HOUSE**

Canvas 242·3 × 184·2

Wellington (see Derby P709) bought Apsley House (now the Wellington Museum) in 1817; the furniture in P632 remains there. John Gurwood (1790–1845), a friend and distant relation of the 4th Marquess of Hertford, who fought with Wellington in the Napoleonic campaigns, became his private secretary and edited the Wellington *Despatches* (1834–38). Probably the picture exhibited at the RA in 1840 as *Apsley House: The Duke of Wellington explaining to the compiler of his despatches the date of that which described the Battle of Waterloo.* Another version (271 × 184) was sold in London in 1924.

Purchased by the 4th Marquess of Hertford 1859

P632

# Charles-Louis MULLER
## 1815–1892

b. and d. Paris; pupil of Cogniet and Gros, q.v.; historical and romantic painter.

P605

### P605   AN EASTERN WOMAN LOOKING IN A MIRROR

Signed: *C.L. Muller*

Canvas 30·8 × 27·6

Acquired by 1872

# Bartolomé Esteban MURILLO
## 1617–1682

b. and d. Seville; pupil of Juan del Castillo; save for brief visits to Madrid, before 1650 and in 1658, he worked in Seville where he helped found the Academy in 1660; influenced by Rubens, q.v., Van Dyck, q.v., and Velasquez, q.v., but his soft *sfumato* and gentle characterisation provided a distinct contribution to Spanish painting, and were particularly prized in the 19th century.

P3

### P3   THE VIRGIN IN GLORY WITH SAINTS ADORING

Canvas 71·1 × 52·4

The Saints are, from the left, John the Baptist, Justa and Rufina (the patron Saints of Seville), and Francis. A drawing by Murillo for these four figures was in the Royal Institute of Cornwall, Truro (last sold in London in 1965); it has been dated in the later 1670s which may, therefore, be the date of P3.

Purchased by the 4th Marquess of Hertford 1843

**P14 THE MARRIAGE OF THE VIRGIN**

Panel 76·8 × 56·5

For the same subject see Champaigne P119;
Joseph here appears on the right and Mary on
the left. Probably painted in the 1670s.

Purchased by the 4th Marquess of Hertford
1848

**P34 THE ADORATION OF THE
SHEPHERDS**

Signed: *Bar^{me} Murillo f.*

Canvas 148·0 × 219·7

P14

Together with P46 and P97 and four other
Murillos (*Immaculate Conception*, Nelson-Atkins
Gallery, Kansas City; *Rest on the Flight*,
Wrotham Park; *Penitent Magdalen*, Wallraf-
Richartz Museum, Cologne; a *St John*, pos-
sibly that formerly at Grosvenor House), P34
was bequeathed to the Capuchin Convent at
Genoa in 1674 by Giovanni Bielato, a Genoese
merchant. All were probably painted *c.* 1670.
The pictures were brought to England in 1805
when they were replaced in the church and
convent by slightly smaller copies. An oil
sketch for P34 (canvas 27 × 35) is in the
Musée Grobet-Labadie, Marseille.

Purchased by the 4th Marquess of Hertford
1846

P34

**P46   JOSEPH AND HIS BRETHREN**

Signed: *Bar^{us} Murillo f.*

Canvas 152·1 × 227·0

The subject is taken from *Genesis* xxxvii, 22–24. See P34.

Purchased by the 4th Marquess of Hertford 1854

P46

**P58   THE HOLY FAMILY WITH ST JOHN THE BAPTIST**

Canvas 169·5 × 132·1

Probably painted in the 1660s.

Purchased by the 4th Marquess of Hertford 1849

P58

## P68    THE ANNUNCIATION

Canvas 189·9 × 136·2

Probably painted between 1668 and 1675. For the same subject, cf. Champaigne P134.

Purchased by the 4th Marquess of Hertford 1843

P68

## P97    THE CHARITY OF ST THOMAS OF VILLANUEVA

Canvas 153·7 × 152·4

See P34. Thomas of Villanueva (1488–1555), Archbishop of Valencia, noted for his philanthropy, was canonised in 1658. Murillo painted four other scenes from his life in the 1670s, two of which are in the Seville Museum.

Purchased by the 4th Marquess of Hertford 1848

P97

P105

## P105  THE ASSUMPTION OF THE VIRGIN

Canvas 65·7 × 41·3

The three Maries appear behind the tomb and the twelve apostles on either side.

Purchased by the 4th Marquess of Hertford 1848

P133

## P133  THE VIRGIN AND CHILD

Canvas 107·3 × 80·0

Painted in the early 1670s; the Virgin is similar to one in the *Annunciation* in the Seville Museum no. 82, and the Child has the same features as one of the angels in an *Assumption* in the same Museum no. 79; P133 was copied by Domingo Martinez as part of a more elaborate composition. Previously catalogued as School of Murillo, the revised attribution was argued convincingly by Angulo in 1975.

Purchased by the 4th Marquess of Hertford 1849

## Attributed to MURILLO

## P136  THE VIRGIN AND CHILD WITH A ROSARY

Canvas 110·5 × 81·0

Acquired by the 4th Marquess of Hertford by 1857

P136

## Follower of MURILLO

**P104    THE VIRGIN AND CHILD WITH (?) ST ROSALIE**

Canvas 70·8 × 83·8

Acquired by the 4th Marquess of Hertford by 1859

P104

## After MURILLO

**P13   THE VIRGIN AND CHILD**

Canvas 167·0 × 111·1

Copy of the painting in the Prado, Madrid (no. 975, *The Virgin with the Rosary*).

Purchased by the 4th Marquess of Hertford 1858

P13

## Jean-Marc NATTIER
### 1685–1766

b. and d. Paris; pupil of his father, Marc Nattier, and at the Académie; portrait painter who frequently employed mythological characterisations; particularly favoured by the daughters of Louis XV.

P453

## P453   THE COMTESSE DE TILLIÈRES

Signed: *Nattier Pnx$^t$ 1750*

Canvas 80·6 × 64·1

Michelle Françoise Julie de Tillières (1715–57) had m. the marquis de Tillières in 1730; he became *Maréchal de Camp* in 1744.

Acquired by 1872

P456

## P456   MLLE DE CLERMONT AT HER BATH

Signed: *Nattier pinxit 1733*

Canvas 110·2 × 105·7

Marie Anne de Bourbon (1697–1741), d. of Louis III duc de Bourbon, secretly m. Louis de Melun, duc de Joyeuse, in 1724, but within a few days he was accidentally killed while hunting; the story was later told by Mme. de Genlis (*Mlle. de Clermont*, 1802). Nattier also painted her in 1729 as a nymph reclining on a pitcher of Chantilly mineral water (Musée Condé); he shows her *à la Turque* in P456 (cf. C. van Loo P451).

Purchased by Sir Richard Wallace 1872

P461

## P461   MLLE DE CHATEAURENAUD

Signed: *Nattier pnx$^t$ 1755*

Canvas 81·9 × 65·4

Marie Charlotte de Chateaurenaud was lady-in-waiting to the daughters of Louis XV.

Acquired by 1872

## After NATTIER

### P414   A NOVICE OF THE ORDER OF THE SAINT ESPRIT

Canvas 83·2 × 61·6

The costume is identical to that worn in *Le comte de Toulouse en habit de novice du Saint-Esprit*, 1693 (Chantilly, attributed to L. de Boullogne); the presence of the mantle on the sofa in P414 would indicate an impending investiture. The subject is possibly Louis, duc d'Orléans (1703–53, son of the Regent). A reduced version of the portrait by Nattier (239 × 179, sd 1732) is in the Gulbenkian Foundation, Lisbon; a version, the same size as P414, was sold in Paris in 1970 as by L-M. van Loo. In a painting shown in the Salon of 1817, Garneray transposed the novice and his page in P414 to the *galerie dorée* of the Hôtel de Toulouse (Banque de France).

Acquired by 1872

P414

### P437   MARIE LESCZYNSKA, QUEEN CONSORT OF FRANCE

Canvas 55·9 × 49·5

Marie Lesczynska (1703–68), d. of King Stanislas of Poland, m. Louis XV in 1725; she bore him seven children and led a homely existence at Versailles, reflected in the informality of Nattier's portrait. P437 is a reduced copy of a portrait first exhibited in 1748, of which there are autograph versions in the Musée de Dijon and at Versailles.

Purchased by Sir Richard Wallace 1872

P437

## Peeter NEEFFS the elder
### active 1605–d. between 1656 and 1661

Probably b. and d. Antwerp; worked in Antwerp where he was probably a pupil of H. van Steenwyck I; painter of church interiors.

P152

**P152    INTERIOR OF ANTWERP CATHEDRAL**

Signed: *Peeter Neeffs*

Panel 48·9 × 64·5

Looking east, the triple-aisled nave appearing very narrow. The figures are said to be by Frans Francken the younger (1581–1642).

In the collection of the 3rd Marquess of Hertford

# Aernout (Aert) van der NEER
## 1603/4–1677

Painted in Amsterdam from *c.* 1635, having begun life in family service; kept a wine-shop between 1658–62; landscape painter, father of Eglon Hendrick, q.v.

P159

**P159    A WINTER SCENE**

Signed: *AVDN*

Canvas 62·2 × 76·2

(HdG 508)

Acquired by 1872

P161

**P161    A CANAL SCENE BY MOONLIGHT**

Signed: *AVN*

Canvas 59·7 × 73·7

(HdG 235)

Acquired by 1872

P200

**P200    A RIVER SCENE: AFTERNOON**

Signed: *AVDN*

Panel 23·5 × 37·8

(HdG 56)

Purchased by (Sir) Richard Wallace 1861

**P217   A SKATING SCENE**

Signed: *AVDN*

Canvas 54·9 × 69·5

(HdG 509)

Purchased by the 4th Marquess of Hertford 1849

P217

## After A. van der NEER

**P157   A RIVER SCENE BY MOONLIGHT**

Inscribed: *AVDN*

Canvas 50·8 × 73·0

Probably the work of a 19th-century imitator. (HdG 234)

Purchased by the 4th Marquess of Hertford 1843

P157

**P184   SCENE ON A CANAL**

Panel 14·0 × 24·1

Possibly a 19th-century copy of a lost original (HdG 318) which was engraved by Zingg in 1763. (HdG 55)

Acquired by 1872

P184

## Eglon Hendrik van der NEER
### 1634?–1703

b. Amsterdam, d. Dusseldorf; pupil of his father Aernout, q.v., and J. van Loo; worked in Amsterdam, Brussels (1679–89) and Düsseldorff (from 1690) where he was court painter to the Elector Palatine.

**P243   A LADY IN RED DRAWING**

Panel 28·3 × 25·4

(HdG 32)

Acquired by 1872

P243

# William Andrews NESFIELD
## 1793–1881

b. Chester-le-Street, d. London; fought in the Peninsula War; landscape gardener and a member of the Royal Society of Painters in Water-Colours.

P703

**P703  KILCHURN CASTLE, LOCH AWE**

Signed: *W.A.N.*

Water-colour 26·4 × 36·5

Purchased by the 4th Marquess of Hertford 1863

# Caspar NETSCHER
## 1635/6–1684

b. Prague, d. The Hague; studied at Arnhem with H. Coster and ter Borch, q.v.; in Bordeaux 1659–61; settled in The Hague by 1662; in the 1660s painted genre, religious and classical subjects, but later turned to small-scale portraiture.

P167

**P167  A LADY WITH AN ORANGE**

Signed: *C.Netscher 1681*

Canvas 48·3 × 39·4

(HdG 377)

Purchased by Sir Richard Wallace 1872

P204

**P204  A LADY WITH A WATCH**

Panel 16·2 × 13·7

(HdG 378)

Acquired by 1872

**P212    A CHILD PLUCKING A ROSE**
Panel 35·6 × 27·0
Pendant to P214. (HdG 454, 457)
Acquired by 1872

P212

**P214    A LADY PLAYING THE GUITAR**
Signed: *C. Netscher 1669*
Panel 35·6 × 27·6
Pendant to P212. (HdG 58, 59)
Acquired by 1872

P214

**P237    THE LACE-MAKER**
Signed: *C. Netscher 1664*
Canvas 34·3 × 28·3
Etched by Pieter de Mare (1757–96); a copy of
the print is also in the Collection, P773
(22·2 × 16·5, inscribed *P. de M. f*). (HdG 48)

P237                        P773

# Gilbert Stuart NEWTON
## 1794–1835

b. Halifax, Nova Scotia, d. Chelsea; studied at Boston with his uncle, Gilbert
Stuart; travelled in Italy and visited Paris before attending RA schools 1817;
narrative painter.

P617

**P617   THE GENTLE STUDENT**

Signed: *G.S. Newton 1829*

Panel 30·5 × 25·1

Engraved by C. Rolls with the present title.

Purchased by the 4th Marquess of Hertford 1859

# Joan van NOORT

*c.* 1620–after 1676

b. Amsterdam; influenced by Rembrandt, q.v., but of diverse styles in his maturity; painted portraits, genre and history pieces.

P20

**P20   A  BOY  WITH  A  HAWK  AND LEASH**

Canvas 83·2 × 67·0

Probably painted in the 1660s.

Acquired by 1872

P96

**P96   A BOY WITH A HAWK**

Canvas 64·8 × 53·3

Probably painted in the 1660s. Cleaned and restored 1977.

Acquired by 1872

# NORTH ITALIAN SCHOOL
## first half 16th century

**P541    A MAN IN BLACK**

Panel 85·4 × 64·5

Probably painted 1520–30. Previously attributed to Bartolommeo Veneto. The carved frame, dated 1543, did not originally belong to P541.

Purchased by Sir Richard Wallace 1872(?)

P541

**P542    YOUNG MAN WITH A LUTE**

Panel 95·6 × 69·8

The sitter is shown as a connoisseur of sculpture as well as a musician.

P542

# Wijnand Jan Joseph NUYEN
## 1813–1839

b. and d. The Hague; pupil of A. Schelfhout, q.v.; painted land- and seascapes.

### P310   RIVER SCENE

Signed: *W. J. J. Nuyen f. 38*
Canvas 90·5 × 116·2
Purchased by the 4th Marquess of Hertford
1870

P310

# Adriaen van OSTADE
## 1610–1685

b. and d. Haarlem; pupil of F. Hals, q.v., with Brouwer, q.v.; worked in Haarlem; a painter and etcher of peasant-scenes, he also painted some portraits and Biblical scenes.

P169

### P169   INTERIOR WITH PEASANTS

Signed: *A.V. Ostade 1663*
Panel 34·3 × 40·0
(HdG 464)
Acquired by the 3rd Marquess of Hertford by 1829

**P202   BUYING FISH**

Signed: *A. Ostade 1661*

Canvas 41·3 × 36·5

(HdG 119, 502)

Purchased by the 4th Marquess of Hertford 1843

P202

## After A. van OSTADE

**P756   BOORS CAROUSING**

Inscribed: *AV Ostade 1656*

Canvas 46·7 × 39·4

Inferior version of the picture sd 1660 at Dresden. A second version, reduced in height, was in a private collection, New York, in 1966. (HdG under 628, as a copy)

Purchased by the 4th Marquess of Hertford 1845

P756

## Isack van OSTADE
### 1621–1649

b. and d. Haarlem; pupil of his brother Adriaen, q.v., whose style he imitated in his early years; his later work centred on outdoor scenes.

**P17   A MARKET PLACE**

Panel 58·4 × 80·6

(HdG 128)

Purchased by the 4th Marquess of Hertford 1843

P17

## P73   A WINTER SCENE

Signed: *Isack van Ostade*

Canvas 87·3 × 107·9

(HdG 255)

Acquired by 1872

P73

# After I. van OSTADE

## P21   A VILLAGE SCENE

Panel 66·7 × 84·1

Copy (or, possibly, replica) of the picture sd 1645 in the National Gallery, Washington. (HdG 23, as either original replica or old copy)

Acquired by the 4th Marquess of Hertford by 1857

P21

# Jean-Baptiste OUDRY
## 1686–1755

b. Paris, d. Beauvais; pupil of his father, Jacques, of De Serre and of Largillierre; began as a history and portrait painter but turned to animal and hunting scenes; designer and painter for the Beauvais tapestry manufactory, and its Director 1733–34; *Inspecteur* of the Gobelins manufactory from 1736; much patronised by Louis XV; see also *Catalogue of Furniture* F204–207. (Hal N. Opperman, *Jean-Baptiste Oudry*, New York, 1977)

### P624   A  HAWK  ATTACKING  WILD DUCK

Canvas 196·8 × 130·2

A composition known in several versions, the best being in the Schwerin museum, sd 1740 (129 × 162); P624 is considered by Opperman to be a studio production, Oudry having worked on the birds. It cannot be the painting sent to Schwerin in 1734 (which was much smaller) as previously stated. A drawing for the right-hand duck is at Schwerin (Opperman P298).

P624

### P625   DOG AND PHEASANTS

Signed: *J.B. Oudry 1748*

Canvas 119·4 × 154·0

Together with P627, P629 and P631, one of four overdoors painted for the *intendant des finances* Trudaine (see also Boucher P482) in 1747–48 and exhibited at the Salon of 1748. (Opperman P263)

Acquired by 1872

P625

## P626   THE DEAD WOLF

Signed: *Peint par J.B. Oudry 1721*

Canvas 196·5 × 261·3

One of Oudry's finest compositions; pendant
to P630. Studio replicas of both are in the
Château de Condé-en-Brie (each with more
space above, 254 × 254). A copy of P626 was
sold in Paris in 1964 (230 × 290), and an oil
sketch was in a private collection in Paris in
1936. (Opperman P389)

P626

## P627   A HAWK ATTACKING PARTRIDGES

Signed: *J.B. Oudry 1747*

Canvas 119·4 × 153·7

See P625. Considered by Opperman to show
the collaboration of an assistant, identified as
the artist's son, Jacques-Charles; while the
hawk is clearly by the master, the rabbit could
be by the son. A drawing for the hawk is in the
Schwerin museum. (Opperman P293)

Acquired by 1872

P627

## P629   A FOX IN THE FARMYARD

Signed: *J.B. Oudry 1748*

Canvas 119·1 × 153·7

See P625. Preliminary drawings for the composition, dated 1746 and 1748 are at Berlin-
Dahlem and in a private collection respec-
tively. A weak replica is at Waddesdon.
(Opperman P294)

Acquired by 1872

P629

### P630   THE DEAD ROE

Signed: *Peint par J.B. Oudry 1721*

Canvas 196·5 × 261·3

Pendant to P626, q.v., and of comparably high quality. Three other versions are recorded. (Opperman P388)

P630

### P631   WILD DUCK AROUSED

Signed: *J.B. Oudry 1748*

Canvas 118·1 × 153·7

See P625. As with P627 from this series, Opperman suspects that Oudry *fils* here collaborated with his father, painting the dog. (Opperman P223)

Acquired by 1872

P631

# Dominique-Louis PAPETY
## 1815–1849

b. and d. Marseille; painter of historical and genre scenes.

**P567   AN ITALIAN CONTADINA**

Signed: DOM. PAPETY

Panel 32·7 × 24·1

Acquired by 1872

P567

**P600   HE LOVES ME, HE LOVES ME NOT**

Signed: PAPETY 48

Panel 32·7 × 24·1

Purchased by the 4th Marquess of Hertford 1851

P600

**P611   THE TEMPTATION OF ST HILARION**

Signed: PAPETY

Panel 50·5 × 64·8

Hilarion, a hermit Saint, lived near Gaza and overcame all temptations to abandon his austere existence; St Anthony Abbot was his inspiration.

Acquired by 1872

P611

P673

**P673    ROMAN CONTADINA AND CHILD**

Signed: DOM. PAPETY

Water-colour 24·4 × 19·4

Acquired by 1872

P711

**P711    A CHINESE GIRL**

Signed: DOM PAPETY

Water-colour 22·2 × 27·3

Evidently a European model in chinese dress.

Acquired by 1872

## School of PARMA
### second quarter 16th century

P552

**P552    THE HOLY FAMILY**

Panel 26·4 × 18·7

A mannerist composition, reflecting the influence of Roman/Parmesan painting of the 1520s.

## Jean-Baptiste-Joseph PATER
### 1695–1736

b. Valenciennes, d. Paris; pupil of Guidé at Valenciennes and Watteau in Paris; *agréé* by the Académie 1728, he became a painter of *fête galantes* wholly influenced by Watteau; his early death was brought on by overwork and, it was said, a miserly temperament. (F. Ingersoll-Smouse, *Pater*, Paris, 1928)

## P380   WATCHING THE DANCE

Canvas 54·6 × 64·8

(Ingersoll-Smouse 231)

Purchased by the 4th Marquess of Hertford 1855

P380

## P383   A CONCERT

Canvas 57·1 × 46·7

*En suite* with P386, P397 and P400; the four were in the collection of the président de Ségur in 1739 when they were engraved (in reverse) by Filloeul. His prints were announced as representing '*les plaisirs les plus ordinaires de la jeunesse*'. P383 was engraved as *Le concert amou-reux*. (Ingersoll-Smouse 25)

P383

## P386   THE SWING

Canvas 57·1 × 47·3

See P383; engraved as *La conversation inter-essante*. (Ingersoll-Smouse 276)

P386

P397

### P397  THE DANCE

Canvas 57·5 × 46·7

See P383. Engraved as *La danse*. (Ingersoll-Smouse 228)

Acquired by 1872

P400

### P400  BLIND MAN'S BUFF

Canvas 57·5 × 46·4

See P383. Engraved as *Le colin maillard*. A version, reversed like the engraving, was at Swinton. (Ingersoll-Smouse 295)

Acquired by 1872

P405

### P405  THE BOUDOIR

Canvas 33·0 × 41·3

Probably a literary subject and possibly from La Fontaine (cf. Lancret P409), but not related to any Filloeul engraving. (Ingersoll-Smouse 481)

Purchased by the 4th Marquess of Hertford 1868

P406

### P406  CONVERSATION GALANTE BY A FOUNTAIN

Canvas 66·0 × 82·6

(Ingersoll-Smouse 50)

## P424   FÊTE IN A PARK

Canvas 54·6 × 66·7

A composition used several times, with minor variations, by Pater (e.g. at Kenwood and Schloss Charlottenburg, Berlin). (Ingersoll-Smouse 36)

Purchased by the 4th Marquess of Hertford 1865

P424

## P426   BATHING PARTY IN A PARK

Canvas 64·1 × 85·1

(Ingersoll-Smouse 327 bis)

P426

## P452   THE VIVANDIÈRES OF BREST

Canvas 47·6 × 60·3

This scene of soldiers resting was engraved (the central part only) by Le Bas in 1760 as *Les vivandières de Brest* (the camp-followers of Brest). (Ingersoll-Smouse 405)

Purchased by Sir Richard Wallace 1872

P452

## P458   CONVERSATION GALANTE

Canvas 47·6 × 40·6

(Ingersoll-Smouse 31)

P458

P460

### P460 FÊTE GALANTE

Canvas 53·3 × 64·5

(Ingersoll-Smouse 39)

Purchased by the 4th Marquess of Hertford 1863

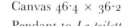

### P472 THE BATH

Canvas 46·4 × 36·2

Pendant to *La toilette* (47 × 37·5, Louvre). A version reduced in height engraved by Surugue in 1744 as *Le plaisir d'été*; further versions are known. (Ingersoll-Smouse 307)

Purchased by the 4th Marquess of Hertford 1852

P472

# August Xaver Karl PETTENKOFEN
## 1822–1889

b. and d. Vienna; studied in the Vienna Academy under L. Kupelweisser; worked in Vienna, making several visits to Paris and Italy; knighted in 1874.

P338

### P338 ROBBERS IN A CORNFIELD

Signed: *Pettenkofen 1852*

Panel 29·8 × 23·5

Commissioned in Vienna in 1851, P338 was finished in Paris the following year.

Purchased by the 4th Marquess of Hertford 1863

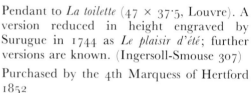

# After PETTENKOFEN

**P621   THE AMBUSCADE**
Inscribed: *A.P. 1846*
Board 20·3 × 26·0
Considered by Weixlgaertner to be a forgery.
Acquired by 1872

P621

# Isidore-Alexandre-Auguste PILS
## 1813–1875

b. Paris, d. Douarnenez; studied under Lethière and Picot; fought in the Crimean war; painter of military and history subjects.

**P665   AN ARAB ENCAMPMENT**
Signed: *I. Pils*
Water-colour 24·4 × 35·6
Acquired by 1872

P665

# Johann Georg PLATZER (Plazer)
## 1704–1761

b. and d. St Michael in Eppan; worked in Vienna, specialising in small history subjects painted on copper.

**P634   THE RAPE OF HELEN**
Signed: *J.G. Plazer*
Copper 40·3 × 59·7
Helen, wife of Menelaus, King of Sparta, is abducted by Paris, son of Priam, and taken to Troy, thereby precipitating the Trojan War (the subject of Homer's *Iliad*).
Purchased by Sir Richard Wallace 1872

P634

# POLIDORO da Caravaggio

## 1492–1543

b. Caravaggio, d. Messina; pupil and assistant of Raphael in Rome; following the sack of Rome, moved to Naples 1527; a decorative, mannerist painter, specialising in monochrome house-façade paintings informed by a deep understanding of the antique.

P775

### P775   STUDY OF FOUR DRAPED FIGURES

Red chalk 11·1 × 15·9

Inscribed below: *Rafaelle 106.*

A study for a figure group which appeared on the left of a grisaille decoration in the Vatican, now destroyed; it was engraved, in reverse, by P. Santi Bartoli (1635–1700). The number *106* may indicate that P775 was once in the collection of Pierre Crozat (who possessed over 280 drawings by Polidoro, although P775 was not, apparently, considered to be one of them). See also Maratti, P774.

# Antonio del POLLAIUOLO, after

## *c.* 1432–1498

b. Florence, d. Rome; pupil of the goldsmith Bartoluccio, influenced by Andrea del Castagno; sculptor, goldsmith, engraver and painter, often in combination with his brother Piero.

P762

### P762   LAMENTATION OVER A DEAD HERO

Pen and bistre 27·6 × 43·8

A contemporary imitation or copy of high quality; the subject has been described as *The Death of Gattamelata* (e.g. in the reversed engraving by M. C. Prestel 1777). Engraved in reverse by Jacopo Francia or Pollaiuolo himself, and by A. Claessen 1535. Berenson recorded an inferior copy at Munich, and listed P762 under Pollajuolo (Antonio), School (*Drawings of the Florentine Painters*, 1903 and 1938, no. 1945).

Purchased by Sir Richard Wallace 1872

# Hendrick POT
## *c.* 1585–1657

b. Haarlem, d. Amsterdam; worked in Haarlem; visited London 1632–33; settled in Amsterdam *c.* 1650; painter of small-scale guardroom and 'merry company' scenes.

### P192   A MERRY COMPANY AT TABLE

Signed: HP (in monogram)

Panel 58·4 × 81·6

Probably painted *c.* 1630; a brothel scene, cf. no. 1278 in the National Gallery.

Acquired by 1872

P192

# Paulus POTTER
## 1625–1654

b. Enkhuizen, d. Amsterdam; pupil of his father, Pieter; worked in The Hague, Delft and Amsterdam; animal painter.

### P189   HERDSMEN WITH THEIR CATTLE

Signed: *Paulus Potter f. 1648*

Panel 37·5 × 42·2

A drawing from this composition, sd 1650, is in the British Museum (Hind 2). A version, using the same hut, is in the Assheton-Bennett collection, Manchester, sd 1649. (HdG 73)

Purchased by the 4th Marquess of Hertford 1865

P189

### P219   THE MILKMAID

Signed: *Paulus Potter A. 1646*

Panel 37·8 × 50·2

(HdG 93)

Acquired by 1872

P219

P252

## P252   CATTLE IN STORMY WEATHER

Signed: *Paulus Potter f. 1653*

Panel 39·1 × 34·3

The group of cattle reappears, for example, in *Four Cows in a meadow* (Rijksmuseum, Amsterdam, sd 1651) (HdG 40, 41, 44a)

Purchased by the 4th Marquess of Hertford 1858

# Frans POURBUS the elder
## 1545–1581

b. Bruges, d. Antwerp; pupil of his father Pieter, q.v., and of Frans Floris in Antwerp; painter of history subjects and portraits; his son, Frans the younger, became court-painter to Queen Marie de Médicis in Paris.

P26

## P26   A GENTLEMAN

Panel 99·4 × 71·1

Inscribed (twice) AN° DNI-1574 and F. POURBUS and *D: of Alencon | 1574*; the duc d'Alençon (1554–84), younger brother of Charles IX and Henri III, is most unlikely to be the sitter (who seems too old, and too healthy for a late Valois).

# Pieter Jansz POURBUS
## 1523–1584

b. Gouda, d. Bruges; travelled in Italy, settled in Bruges 1543; painter of portraits and histories, also a surveyor and engineer; father of Frans the elder, q.v.

### P531   AN ALLEGORICAL LOVE FEAST

Signed: PETRVS POVRBVS FACIEBAT (and with cypher)

Panel 134·0 × 206·7

The figures are labelled, and illustrate the complexities of love. From the left: Adonis with Affectio; Acontius with Cordialitas; Sapiens with Fidutia, and Daphnis with Reverentia. The first three are also attended by the three Graces. Daphnis has been playing a song by T. Susato, published in 1543. The group begins with Cupid and ends with Folly. The table bears a relief, probably of Callisto changed into a bear (Ovid, *Metamorphoses* ii). Related compositions are in the Kunstmuseum, Basel, and the Museo Civico, Verona.

Purchased by Sir Richard Wallace 1872

P531

# Nicolas POUSSIN
## 1594–1665

b. Les Andelys (Seine Maritime), d. Rome; studied under Varin *c*. 1611–12 in Normandy, and Elle in Paris; settled in Rome 1624 but revisited Paris 1641–2; painted Biblical and mythological scenes, influenced by Raphael, Titian and the antique.

P108

### P108 A DANCE TO THE MUSIC OF TIME

Canvas 84·8 × 107·6

Painted *c*. 1639–40; cleaned and restored 1976. Engraved by B. Picart (1673–1733) as *L'Image de la Vie Humaine*. From the left the dancers represent: Pleasure, Poverty, Riches and Work (only poverty is male; the implication is that, through work, poverty becomes riches which allow pleasure). The figure of Time plays the lyre; a two-headed term (the past and the future) and putti, with an hourglass and blowing bubbles, further emphasise the passage of time. In the sky Aurora pulls the chariot of Apollo, followed by the hours. (A. Blunt, *Burlington Magazine*, December 1976, pp. 844–47)

Purchased by the 4th Marquess of Hertford 1845

# Pierre-Paul PRUD'HON
## 1758–1823

b. Cluny, d. Paris; pupil of Devosges at Dijon, and of the Académie in Paris 1780–82; studied in Rome 1785–89; deeply influenced by Correggio and Leonardo, see also Mayer above.

P264

### P264 PUPPIES

Panel 21·9 × 15·9

An early work, probably *c*. 1780–82. Engraved by Roger as *Oh! Les jolis petits chiens*. A larger version (65 × 54) sold in 1868, had as a pendant *Mange, mon petit, mange*, now in a private collection.

Acquired by 1872

## P272    THE ASSUMPTION OF THE VIRGIN

Canvas 32·4 × 24·1

A sketch for the altarpiece commissioned for the chapel of the Tuileries in 1816, now in the Louvre (216 × 149, exhibited in the Salon of 1819). A drawing in the Metropolitan Museum, New York, shows an earlier preparatory stage. The ring of putti in P272 was suppressed from the final design by order of the Grande Aumônerie.

Purchased by the 4th Marquess of Hertford 1843

P272

## P295    THE ZEPHYR

Canvas 21·6 × 15·9

A reduced version of the *Jeune Zéphyr se balançant au-dessus de l'eau* in the Louvre (130 × 98, sd 1814; another grisaille version, 128 × 97, also in the Louvre). A preliminary drawing is in the Musée de Dijon.

Acquired by 1872

P295

## P313    THE HAPPY MOTHER

Canvas 24·1 × 17·5

A sketch for *La mère heureuse* by Mayer (q.v.) which was exhibited at the Salons of 1810 and 1814 and is now in the Louvre (194 × 147), with *La mère malheureuse* as its pendant.

Purchased by the 4th Marquess of Hertford 1846

P313

P315

### P315   JOSEPHINE BEAUHARNAIS

Canvas 61·6 × 50·5

Josephine Tascher de la Pagerie (1763–1814) m. 1st in 1779 the vicomte de Beauharnais (executed 1794), and 2nd Napoleon I in 1796 (marriage dissolved 1809); she had two daughters and a son by her first husband (see Schopin P568). Probably painted *c*. 1811 when she had retired to Malmaison.

Purchased by the 4th Marquess of Hertford 1864

### P347   VENUS AND ADONIS

Canvas 243·8 × 171·5

Commissioned by the Empress Marie-Louise in 1810 for a salon in the Tuileries, but not installed (the Russian war intervening). Several preliminary drawings are recorded, including one in the Rijksmuseum, Amsterdam, showing just two dogs in the foreground.

Purchased by Sir Richard Wallace 1875

P347

# Adam PYNACKER
## 1621–1673

b. Pijnacker, near Delft, d. Amsterdam; travelled in Italy before 1649 when he was back in Delft; in Schiedam 1658; landscape painter influenced by Both, q.v., and J. Asselijn; see also Both, ascribed, P24.

### P57    LANDSCAPE WITH ANIMALS

Canvas 121·3 × 105·1

(HdG 155)

Acquired by 1872

P57

### P115    LANDSCAPE WITH CATTLE

Signed: *A. Pynacker*

Canvas 81·9 × 70·8

(HdG 156)

Purchased by Sir Richard Wallace 1872

P115

# Denis-Auguste-Marie RAFFET
## 1804–1860

b. Paris, d. Genoa; pupil of Gros, q.v. and Charlet; drew military subjects from the First Republic and the First Empire in water-colour and for lithography.

P731

### P731    SOLDIERS OF THE REPUBLIC

Signed: *Raffet à son ami . . . . 30 juin 1849*

Water-colour 21·6 × 14·9

Acquired by 1874

P737

### P737    THE TRIAL OF MARIE ANTOINETTE

Signed: *Raffet*

Water-colour 9·5 × 13·0

Marie-Antoinette (1755–93), Queen of Louis XVI, was tried by the Revolutionary Tribunal and guillotined in 1793.

Acquired by 1874

P744

### P744    FRENCH INFANTRY IN SQUARE

Signed: *Raffet*

Water-colour 9·5 × 13·0

Acquired by 1874

P745

### P745    NAPOLEON AFTER AUSTERLITZ

Signed: *Raffet 1845*

Water-colour 11·7 × 15·9

The battle of Austerlitz in which Napoleon overcame the Russians and the Austrians, was fought in 1805 and remained his most famous victory.

Acquired by 1874

P747

### P747    SAINT JEAN D'ACRE

Signed: *Raffet*

Water-colour 9·5 × 11·7

Napoleon besieged Saint Jean d'Acre (north of Haifa on the Israeli coast) in 1799 but was repulsed by the Turks and Sir Sidney Smith.

Acquired by 1872

# Allan RAMSAY, after
## 1713–1784

b. Edinburgh, d. Dover; in Italy 1736–38 and 1754–57; worked in London, appointed Principal painter to George III in 1767.

### P560   KING GEORGE III

Canvas 81·3 × 65·1

George III (1738–1820) became King in 1760. A reduced copy of the whole-length by Ramsay painted in 1761–62 now in Buckingham Palace.

P560

# Jean RAOUX
## 1677–1734

b. Montpellier, d. Paris; pupil of Bon Boullogne; in Rome and Venice 1704–16; *agréé* by the Académie 1716; influenced by Dutch 17th-century painting, painted mythologised portraits and genre scenes.

### P128   A LADY AT HER MIRROR

Canvas 81·3 × 66·0

A version on the London art market 1967 was indistinctly signed and dated 1729(?)

Acquired by 1872

P128

# REMBRANDT
## 1606–1669

b. Leiden, d. Amsterdam; pupil of van Swanenburgh at Leiden 1621–23, and of Lastman in Amsterdam 1624; worked in Leiden 1625–31, moved to Amsterdam 1631–32; painted portraits and histories, influencing a generation of Dutch artists by his teaching. (A. Bredius, *Rembrandt*, revised by H. Gerson, 1969; K. Bauch, *Rembrandt*, Berlin, 1966)

P29

### P29   THE ARTIST'S SON, TITUS

Signed: *R...* (incomplete, see below)

Canvas 70·8 × 58·4

Titus van Rijn (1641–68) only child of Rembrandt and his first wife (Saskia) to reach maturity. Painted *c.* 1657; cleaned and restored 1977. Old stretcher marks on the original canvas suggest that the picture has been reduced by approximately 6 cm. down the right-hand edge, and by 3 cm. across the bottom edge; the signature has certainly been cut and the background detail on the right (a stone ledge?) is unresolved; a horizontal shape along the bottom edge might have been a glove. The top corners appear to have been reworked by the artist to suggest an arched top. (Bredius 123: Bauch 419; HdG 704)

Acquired by the 4th Marquess of Hertford by 1857

P52

### P52   THE ARTIST IN A CAP

Signed (inscribed?): *Rembrandt...*

Panel 65·1 × 50·5

The top was originally flat with a semi-circular projection. Painted *c.* 1634–36 (Bauch suggests *c.* 1640). (Bredius 27, Bauch 315, HdG 559)

Purchased by the 4th Marquess of Hertford 1848

## P82    JAN PELLICORNE WITH HIS SON CASPAR

Inscribed: *Rembrant f ͨ*

Canvas 156·5 × 124·5

The identity of the sitters seems first to have been given in 1872; Jan Pellicorne (b. 1597) m. Susanna van Collen (see P90) in 1626; their daughter was born in 1627 and their son was baptised in June 1628. P82 and P90 were cleaned and restored in 1972 revealing a certain hardness of execution (particularly evident in the figures of the children), not altogether inconsistent with the early 1630s. The father's gesture of handing a money-bag to his son seems echoed in the picture on the wall behind showing the blessing of a child by a priest (? a Presentation in the Temple) (Bredius 406; Bauch 533; HdG 666)

Purchased by the 4th Marquess of Hertford 1850

P82

## P90    SUSANNA PELLICORNE WITH HER DAUGHTER

Inscribed: *Rembrant f ͨ 163.*

Canvas 156·5 × 124·1

See P82. The mother hands her daughter a coin from her purse; a basket of fruit behind symbolises a hope for fertility. (Bredius 407; Bauch 534; HdG 667)

Purchased by the 4th Marquess of Hertford 1850

P90

P777                    P203

P229

### P203    THE GOOD SAMARITAN

Signed: *RL 1630*

Panel 24·2 × 19·8 enlarged to 26·4 × 21·3

The subject is taken from *Luke* x, 30–37. Cleaning and restoration in 1976 dispelled doubts concerning authenticity. The subject was etched by Rembrandt in 1633, in reverse, with minor differences (including a prominent defecating dog); a copy of the print is also in the Collection, P777 (25·3 × 20·1 inscribed: *Rembrandt. inventor.et. feecit* (sic). *1633.*; 4th state). (Bredius 545; Bauch 55; HdG 111, all before cleaning; K. Clark, *Burlington Magazine*, December 1976, pp. 806–9)

Acquired by the 3rd Marquess of Hertford by 1836

### P229    LANDSCAPE WITH A COACH

Signed: *Rembrandt*

Panel 47·0 × 66·7

Painted *c.* 1640–41; a threatening autumn landscape with a gentleman regarding the scene from the right. (Bredius 451; Bauch 550; HdG 948, 955c)

Purchased by the 3rd Marquess of Hertford 1823

## Follower of REMBRANDT

### P86    THE CENTURION CORNELIUS

Inscribed: *A° 1655(?)*

Canvas 181·6 × 221·0

The subject is taken from *Acts* x, 1–8; engraved by James Ward 1800 with this title. Ascribed to Rembrandt in the 19th century, an attribution rejected, for example, by Bredius in 1936. The reading of the date, 1655, agrees with the apparent influence of the later Rembrandt, but a generally accepted attribution has yet to be made. Current opinion favours Karel Fabritius (1622–54), a pupil of Rembrandt *c.* 1642 who was working in Delft from *c.* 1651; Karel van der Pluym (*c.* 1625–72), another Rembrandt pupil of the 1640s, active in Leiden, has also been proposed. (HdG 114, as Rembrandt)

Purchased by the 4th Marquess of Hertford 1848

P86

## P201   A YOUNG BOY

Inscribed: *Rembrandt fct 1633*

Panel 21·0 × 17·5

The status of P201, and of several other related studies of the same model, has been questioned by Gerson who considers that the attribution to Rembrandt cannot, in this case, be sustained. The date in the inscription could be correct, and the style approaches that of Flinck, q.v. (Bredius 188; Bauch 149 and HdG 491, as Rembrandt).

P201

# Imitator of REMBRANDT

## P55   AN OFFICER IN A PLUMED HAT

Inscribed: *Rembrandt f.*

Panel 67·0 × 52·4

(Bredius 193, as a suspected Worlidge; Bauch 160, as a somewhat unusual Rembrandt; HdG 558, as Rembrandt).

Purchased by the 4th Marquess of Hertford 1848

P55

# After REMBRANDT

P173

### P173    SELF-PORTRAIT

Inscribed: *Rem ft 1650*

Copper 22·9 × 15·9

Copy of the picture in the Kunsthistorisches Museum, Vienna (Bredius 42, sd 1652).

Purchased by the 4th Marquess of Hertford 1868(?)

# Guido RENI, after
## 1575–1642

b. and d. Bologna; influenced by the Carracci; worked in Rome and Bologna.

P644

### P644    THE VIRGIN AND CHILD WITH ST JOHN

Copper 21·9 × 28·3

Possibly a copy of an unidentified Reni; apparently a 17th-century work.

Acquired by the 4th Marquess of Hertford by 1859

# Joshua REYNOLDS
## 1723–1792

b. Plymouth, d. London; pupil of Hudson in London 1740; in Italy 1749–52; worked in London; knighted in 1769; first President of the Royal Academy, whose Discourses defined a noble academicism, founded on Italian high renaissance and baroque painting; the characterisation of his portraiture was outstanding (see also Roqueplan P603, After Velazquez P4, Westall P566).

## P31    LADY    ELIZABETH    SEYMOUR-CONWAY

Canvas 61·6 × 47·3

The sitter (1754–1825) was the eighth child and fifth daughter of the first Marquess of Hertford; she died unmarried. Painted in 1781, together with P33 below; the Marquess paid for them in 1784.

Purchased by the 1st Marquess of Hertford 1784

P31

## P32    MRS RICHARD HOARE AND HER SON

Canvas 134·0 × 107·9

Susanna Cecilia Dingley (1743–95) m. Richard Hoare (d. 1778) in 1762; their son Henry was b. 7 April 1766 and d. 9 March 1768. Painted 1767–68; a sketch for the heads (74 × 62) was in the Ellesmere collection.

Purchased by the 4th Marquess of Hertford 1859

P32

## P33    FRANCES    SEYMOUR-CONWAY, COUNTESS OF LINCOLN

Canvas 61·9 × 47·0

The sitter (1751–1820) was the seventh child and fourth daughter of the first Marquess of Hertford; she m. the Earl of Lincoln in 1775. See P31.

Purchased by the 1st Marquess of Hertford 1784

P33

P35

## P35   MRS JOHN CARNAC

Canvas 242·9 × 152·4

Elizabeth Catharine (*sic*) Rivett (1751–80) m. General John Carnac (*c.* 1720–1800) in 1769; they sailed to India, where Mrs Carnac died, in April 1776. Painted 1775–76, P35 remained in Reynolds's studio until sold at his death in 1796.

Purchased by the 4th Marquess of Hertford 1861

P36

## P36   MISS JANE BOWLES

Canvas 91·8 × 71·1

The sitter (1772–1812) was the eldest child of the amateur artist Oldfield Bowles of North Aston; she m. Richard Palmer. Painted in 1775; a sketch for the head and shoulders was in the Ellesmere collection.

Purchased by the 4th Marquess of Hertford 1850

## P38   NELLY O'BRIEN

Canvas 127·6 × 101·6

The sitter (d. 1768), a famous courtesan, sat frequently to Reynolds between 1760 and 1767. P38 was probably exhibited in 1763. A second portrait by Reynolds, painted *c.* 1764–67(?) now belongs to the Hunterian Museum, Glasgow.

Purchased by the 2nd Marquess of Hertford 1810

P38

## P40   THE STRAWBERRY GIRL

Canvas 76·2 × 63·5

Painted and exhibited at the RA in 1773; probably the first version of the subject. A second was painted for Lord Carysfort, now at Bowood, differing in the head-dress and background detail. Regarded by Reynolds as one of his 'really original' works.

Purchased by the 4th Marquess of Hertford 1856

P40

## P43   MRS MARY NESBITT, called, WITH A DOVE

Canvas 76·5 × 63·2

Previously called Mrs Arnold Nesbitt, sister of Henry Thrale, but purchased by Lord Hertford as 'Mrs Nesbitt, the actress' whom Reynolds painted as *Circe* in 1781; P43 probably shows the actress, as Hertford supposed. Probably painted in 1781.

Purchased by the 4th Marquess of Hertford 1859

P43

P45

P47

P48

## P45  MRS. MARY ROBINSON ('PERDITA')

Canvas 77·5 × 63·5

For the sitter, see Gainsborough P42 and Romney P37. Painted in 1784 when Mrs Robinson was half-paralysed; she was in France between August 1784 and January 1788. P45 was engraved in 1787 as *Contemplation*. Of many versions, the most important are the oil sketch in the British Art Center, Yale, and the drawing for the head in the British Museum. A second portrait by Reynolds, showing the sitter in her hey-day in 1782 is at Waddesdon; a copy in miniature is in The Wallace Collection, M40.

Purchased by the 4th Marquess of Hertford 1859

## P47  MRS WILLIAM BRADDYLL

Canvas 75·6 × 63·2

Jane Gale (d. 1819) m. William Braddyll (1756–1818) of Conishead Priory, Lancs., in 1776. Painted in 1788. A second portrait showing her with her husband and son, Thomas, was one of Reynolds's last portraits, painted in 1789 (Fitzwilliam Museum, Cambridge).

Purchased by the 4th Marquess of Hertford 1854

## P48  ST JOHN IN THE WILDERNESS

Canvas 128·0 × 102·6

The scroll is inscribed *voice*, a reference to *John* i, 23. Painted *c.* 1776, one of three surviving versions of a subject exhibited at the RA that year. The original is presumed to have been that destroyed by fire at Belvoir Castle in 1816; other versions are now in the Minneapolis Institute of Arts and at Arbury.

Purchased by the 3rd Marquess of Hertford 1813

**P561 WILLIAM 4th DUKE OF QUEENSBERRY**

Canvas 92·1 × 71·4

William Douglas, 3rd Earl of March (1735–1810), became 4th Duke of Queensberry ('Old Q') in 1778; probably the father of Maria Fagnani, the third Marchioness of Hertford, he left property and money to the Hertfords. Painted in 1759, the coronet by his right hand being an Earl's; the collar of the Thistle (he was made K.T. in 1761) is a later addition.

Acquired by the 3rd Marquess of Hertford(?)

P561

# Hyacinthe RIGAUD, studio of
## 1659–1743

b. Perpignan, d. Paris; pupil of Pezet and Ranc at Montpellier; won the Prix de Rome 1682 but did not go to Italy; a successful portrait painter and an influential member of the Académie; maintained a number of assistants in his studio.

**P130 CARDINAL FLEURY**

Canvas 82·2 × 66·0

André-Hercule de Fleury (1653–1743), Bishop of Fréjus 1698–1715, was *premier ministre* of France from 1723 until his death; tutor to the young Louis XV; made a Cardinal 1726. One of many half-length versions of Rigaud's three-quarter length at Versailles, which was probably painted in 1706.

P130

# Léopold-Louis ROBERT
## 1794–1835

b. La Chaux-de-Fonds, Switzerland, d. Venice; pupil of David, worked in Rome; took his own life *'en un accès de défaillance'* (Lamartine).

P590

### P590    THE BRIGAND ON THE WATCH

Signed: *L$^{ld}$ Robert Roma 1825*

Canvas 47·3 × 38·1

Robert's favourite subjects were the brigands from Sonnino imprisoned in Rome in 1819; see also P591 and P592.

Acquired by 1872

P591

### P591    THE BRIGAND ASLEEP

Signed: *L$^{ld}$ Robert Roma 1826*

Canvas 47·3 × 38·1

See P590.

Acquired by 1872

P592

### P592    THE DEATH OF THE BRIGAND

Signed: *L$^{ld}$ Robert Roma 1824*

Canvas 47·6 × 37·8

See P590.

Acquired by 1872

## P615   A NEAPOLITAN FISHERMAN

Signed: $L^{ld}$ *Robert*

Panel 35·6 × 27·0

P615

# Joseph-Nicolas ROBERT-FLEURY
## 1797–1890

b. Cologne d. Paris; pupil of Gros, q.v., Girodet and H. Vernet, q.v.; Director of the École des Beaux-Arts 1864 and of the Académie in Rome 1865.

## P361   CHARLES V AT THE MONASTERY OF YUSTE

Signed: *Robert Fleury 1856*

Canvas 101·6 × 146·1

Charles V (see Flemish School P529) withdrew to a small house near the monastery of Yuste in 1557; here he is begged by the Count of Melilo, on behalf of King Philip II to enter again into the difficult affairs of Spain. On the wall behind appear Titian's portrait of Philip II of 1551 and his 'Gloria' of 1554 (both now in the Prado, Madrid).

Purchased by Sir Richard Wallace 1872

P361

P686

**P686   CARDINAL RICHELIEU**

Signed: *Robt. Fleury 1834*

Water-colour 12·1 × 14·6

Armand-Jean du Plessis, duc de Richelieu (1585–1642), Cardinal 1622 and *premier ministre* until his death. See also Delaroche P320.

Acquired by 1874

P778

**P778   CARDINAL RICHELIEU**

Signed: *R Fleury 183[1?]*

Water-colour 17·5 × 13·0

See P686.

Acquired by 1874

# David ROBERTS
## 1796–1864

b. Edinburgh, d. London; apprenticed to a house-decorator in Edinburgh; scene-painter in London 1822; became a noted painter in oil and water-colour of architectural views from Europe and the near East.

P258

**P258   INTERIOR OF ST. GOMMAR, LIERRE**

Signed: *David Roberts R.A. 1850*

Panel 123·2 × 94·6

From the west; a water-colour by Roberts of the transepts from the north is in a private collection.

Purchased by the 4th Marquess of Hertford 1863

### P587 GRANADA CATHEDRAL: THE CAPILLA REAL

Signed: *David Roberts 1838 Granada*

Panel 47·6 × 37·5

P587

### P659 THE CATHEDRAL AND SEMINARIO, SANTIAGO

Signed: *D. Roberts 1837*

Water-colour 24·8 × 39·4

From the south-west.

Purchased by the 4th Marquess of Hertford 1863

P659

### P680 THE TEMPLE OF JUPITER, BAALBEK

Signed: *David Roberts 1842*

Water-colour 13·7 × 20·6

The ruins of the temple seen from the east.

Purchased by the 4th Marquess of Hertford 1863

P680

### P689 MAINZ CATHEDRAL FROM THE NORTH-WEST

Signed: *D. Roberts 1832*

Water-colour 23·2 × 31·4

Acquired by 1874

P689

### P697 THE GREAT SQUARE TETUAN, MOROCCO

Signed: *David Roberts 1837*

Water-colour 27·6 × 39·4

A view from the Jews' quarter on the occasion of the marriage of the Governor's son in April 1833; a drawing admired by Turner.

Purchased by the 4th Marquess of Hertford 1863

P697

# ROMAN SCHOOL
## 16th century

P553

**P553   THE HOLY FAMILY**

Panel 44·5 × 31·4

Formerly attributed to Giulio Romano.

Acquired by 1872

# George ROMNEY
## 1734–1802

b. Dalton, d. Kendal; pupil of Steele at Kendal; moved to London 1762; in Italy 1773; did not exhibit at the RA, but a serious rival to Reynolds as a portrait painter.

P37

**P37   MRS. MARY ROBINSON ('PERDITA')**

Canvas 75·6 × 63·2

For the sitter, see Gainsborough P42 and Reynolds P45. Painted in 1781, an engraving by J. R. Smith published 25 August that year. A second portrait by Romney, painted 1781–82, remains unidentified.

Purchased by the 2nd Marquess of Hertford 1810

# Camille-Joseph-Étienne ROQUEPLAN
## 1803–1855

b. Mallemort, d. Paris; studied at the École des Beaux-Arts from 1818 and under Gros, q.v., and Pujol; popular landscape and genre painter.

**P285    THE LION IN LOVE**

Signed: *C^{lle} Roqueplan 1836*

Canvas 194·9 × 152·4

The subject is taken from La Fontaine, *Fables* iii, 17: the amorous, but gullible, lion has his claws (and teeth) removed. Exhibited in the Salon of 1836. A preliminary crayon sketch is in the Musée Magnin, Dijon.

Purchased by the 4th Marquess of Hertford 1853

P285

P571

**P571    A SENTIMENTAL CONVERSATION**

Signed: *C^{lle} Roqueplan 1843*
Panel 41·9 × 33·7
Acquired by 1872

P583

**P583    SUMMER PLEASURES**

Signed: *C. Roqueplan*
Canvas 45·4 × 30·2
Acquired by 1872

P595

**P595    CASTEL GANDOLFO: SUNSET**

Signed: *C^{lle} Roqueplan 1832*
Canvas 36·2 × 27·9
Acquired by 1872

**P603    LOUIS-PHILIPPE-JOSEPH, DUC D'ORLÉANS, after Reynolds**

Panel 21·0 × 14·9

The sitter, 'Philippe-Égalité' (1747–93), duc de Chartres 1752, and duc d'Orléans 1785, removed from the Court by Marie-Antoinette for his excessive liberalism, became a close friend of George IV as Prince of Wales (see Hoppner P563); christened *Citoyen Égalité* by the Commune, he was nevertheless guillotined in 1793. A free copy of the portrait painted in 1785 (Buckingham Palace, 238 × 147).

P603

**P609    PEASANTS OF BÉARN**

Signed: *C^{lle} Roqueplan Pau 1846*

Canvas 54·3 × 41·9

Béarn now part of the département of the Basses-Pyrénées, of which Pau is the capital.

Acquired by 1872

P609

**P612    ROUSSEAU AND MLLE. GALLEY GATHERING CHERRIES**

Signed: *C^{lle} Roqueplan 1851*

Panel 66·0 × 47·9

The subject is taken from J-J. Rousseau's *Confessions* i, 4: the nineteen-year-old philosopher falls in love (an affair which ended with a kiss on the hand).

Purchased by the 4th Marquess of Hertford 1853

P612

P652

**P652    THE TIMBER WAGGON**

Signed: $C^{lle}$ *Roqueplan 1832*

Water-colour 30·5 × 21·3

Acquired by 1874

P662

**P662    THE FISHERWOMAN'S CHILDREN**

Signed: *Camille Roqueplan*

Water-colour 17·5 × 25·7

Acquired by 1874

P707

**P707    THE STOLEN KISS**

Signed: *Camille Roqueplan*

Water-colour 26·7 × 21·3

Acquired by 1872

# Salvator ROSA
## 1615–1673

b. Naples, d. Rome; studied in Naples under Fracanzano and Falcone; worked in Rome 1635–39, Florence 1640–49, and in Rome from 1649; his wild, gaunt landscape-settings exerted a considerable influence on 18th-century taste.

### P116  APOLLO AND THE CUMAEAN SYBIL

Signed: *Rosa*

Canvas 175·3 × 261·0

The subject is taken from Ovid, *Metamorphoses*, xiv: Apollo allows her to live for as many years as there are grains of dust in her hands, but since she then repulsed his advances she lived on as an old hag. This fine, late work was owned by Cardinal Mazarin (d. 1661); there is a drawing, and an etching, by Rosa of the central figure group.

Purchased by the 4th Marquess of Hertford 1850

P116

# Pierre-Étienne-Théodore ROUSSEAU
## 1812–1867

b. Paris, d. Barbizon; pupil of Rémond and Lethière; worked in Auvergne 1830 and in Switzerland 1834; settled in Barbizon 1844 where he became one of the leading landscape painters of that school.

**P283   THE FOREST OF FONTAINEBLEAU: MORNING**

Signed: *TH. Rousseau*

Canvas 98·1 × 134·0

Painted *c.* 1848–50. Exhibited in the Salon of 1851 together with the comparable *Sortie de forêt à Fontainebleau* (commissioned by the State in 1848; 142 × 197, Louvre) which shows an evening effect.

Acquired by 1872

P283

# Peeter Pauwel RUBENS
## 1577–1640

b. Siegen, d. Antwerp; trained in Antwerp chiefly by Otho van Veen; worked in Italy 1600–8, thereafter mainly in Antwerp; visited Madrid 1603 and 1628: Paris 1622 and 1625, and London 1629–30 (all for royal commissions); painter and diplomat for the Archduke Albert (d. 1621) and the Archduchess Isabella (d. 1633) from 1609; knighted by Charles I in 1629.

## P63  THE RAINBOW LANDSCAPE

Panel 136·5 × 236·5

Painted *c.* 1636, probably as a pendant to the *Autumn Landscape with a view of Het Steen* (National Gallery, London, no. 66, panel 131 × 230); both were in the Balbi Palace, Genoa, in the 18th century, and both express the extraordinary richness of Rubens's full maturity. A version of P63, probably a preliminary study, is at Munich (panel 92 × 122), and two smaller studies are in a private collection and at Philadelphia.

Purchased by the 4th Marquess of Hertford 1856

P63

## P71  CHRIST ON THE CROSS

Canvas 106·7 × 70·5

Probably painted *c.* 1610; the composition relates very closely to an engraving by Pontius of 1631 from the altarpiece for the Abbey of Tongerloo (now untraced). Another version is in the Fine Arts Museum, Antwerp, dated *c.* 1610 (canvas 219 × 122), and a smaller version is at Philadelphia (panel 49 × 37).

Acquired by 1872

P71

P81

### P81   THE HOLY FAMILY WITH SS. ELIZABETH AND JOHN THE BAPTIST

Panel 138·4 × 102·2

John sits on Elizabeth's (his mother's) knee and is blessed by Jesus, foreshadowing the baptism of Christ. Painted *c.* 1614 for the oratory of the Archduke Albert in the old ducal palace, Brussels (burnt down in 1731). Amongst several versions by inferior hands, two show an extended composition: in the Pinacoteca, Siena (canvas 201 × 123), and in a private collection, Vienna; a small version on copper is at Apsley House.

Purchased by the 4th Marquess of Hertford 1846

P93

### P93   CHRIST'S CHARGE TO PETER

Panel 141·0 × 114·6

The subject is taken from *John* xxi, 16; the three background Saints are probably Paul, John and James. Painted *c.* 1614 for Nicolas Damant (d. 1616) who placed it in the chapel of the Holy Sacrament in the church of St Gudule, Brussels. The composition appears in *A Picture Gallery* by Jan Brueghel II (1601–78) in Philadelphia. Another version is at Pittsburgh.

Purchased by the 4th Marquess of Hertford 1850.

P519

### P519   THE ADORATION OF THE MAGI

Panel 63·5 × 48·3

Sketch for the altarpiece commissioned for the Abbaye Saint-Michel, Antwerp, in 1624 (panel 444 × 336, now in the Fine Arts Museum, Antwerp).

Acquired by 1872

**P520   THE DEFEAT AND DEATH OF MAXENTIUS**

Panel 38·4 × 64·5

P520

Maxentius, Emperor of Rome 306–12, defeated by Constantine outside Rome at the Milvian Bridge where he perished in the river Tiber. One of a series of twelve sketches (all formerly in the Orléans collection) for tapestries illustrating *The History of Constantine* commissioned by Louis XIII in 1622.

Purchased by the 4th Marquess of Hertford 1856

**P521   THE ADORATION OF THE MAGI**

Panel 50·2 × 36·5

Sketch for the altarpiece commissioned for the Convent Church of the White Sisters of Louvain, installed in 1633 (canvas 330 × 248, now in the Chapel of King's College, Cambridge).

Acquired by 1872

P521

**P522   THE TRIUMPHAL ENTRY OF HENRI IV INTO PARIS**

Panel 21·3 × 37·1

P522

Henri IV (1553–1610) entered Paris as King in 1594, having overcome the forces of the Catholic League; he m. Marie de Médicis in 1600. Together with P523 and P524, below, P522 is one of six preparatory sketches for a suite of twenty-one pictures illustrating the *History of Henri IV*, commissioned by Marie de Médicis for the Palais du Luxembourg (together with the set of twenty-one illustrating her own history, now in the Louvre). Rubens worked on the Henri IV cycle between 1628 and 1631, when it was discontinued owing to the Queen Mother's exile in Brussels; six large, unfinished canvases were left in Rubens's studio at his death. Another sketch for *The*

*Triumphal Entry* is in the Metropolitan Museum, New York (panel 49 × 85), and the unfinished final picture is in the Uffizi, Florence (canvas 378 × 690).

Purchased by the 4th Marquess of Hertford 1865

P523

## P523   THE BIRTH OF HENRI IV

Panel 21·3 × 9·8

See P522. Henri IV was born in Pau on 14 December 1553; the river-god in the foreground doubtless represents the Gave de Pau: Mars presents a sword to the infant who is nursed by a woman personifying the city of Pau: the sign of Sagittarius (for December) appears above. This would have been the first subject of the cycle.

Purchased by the 4th Marquess of Hertford 1859

P524

## P524   THE MARRIAGE OF HENRI IV AND MARIE DE MÉDICIS

Panel 23·2 × 12·4

See P522. The genius above represents Hymen, god of marriage; the marriage took place in Florence, Marie's home, by proxy on 5 October 1600. Rubens appears to have used Dürer's engraving *The Promenade* as a source for his composition. This would have been the final subject of the cycle.

Purchased by the 4th Marquess of Hertford 1859

## Studio of RUBENS

### P30    ISABELLA BRANT, called

Panel 101·6 × 73·3

Isabella Brant (1591–1626) m. Rubens in 1609 as his first wife. The features do not readily agree with undoubted portraits, but are similar to those in a portrait at Berlin-Dahlem whose identity has also been questioned. P30 appears to be a version of the portrait in the Mauritshuis, The Hague, (panel 96 × 73) which is considered a studio work.

Purchased by the 4th Marquess of Hertford 1853

P30

## Jacob van RUISDAEL
### 1628/9(?)–1682

b. and probably d. Haarlem; probably a pupil of his father and of his uncle, Salomon van Ruysdael; worked in Haarlem, where he was a friend of Berchem, q.v., and in Amsterdam from 1657.

### P50    ROCKY LANDSCAPE

Signed: *JVRuisdael*

Canvas 104·5 × 127·0

Probably painted in the 1660s. (HdG 250a, 721a)

Purchased by the 4th Marquess of Hertford 1861

P50

P56

## P56    LANDSCAPE WITH A WATERFALL

Signed: *JVRuisdael*

Canvas 103·5 × 143·8

Probably painted in the 1660s. Cleaned in 1975. (HdG 251)

Purchased by the 4th Marquess of Hertford 1850

P156

## P156    LANDSCAPE WITH A VILLAGE

Signed: *JVRuisdael*

Canvas 74·6 × 92·4

Probably painted in the 1660s. The castle has recently been identified as Schloss Steinfurt (north of Münster). (HdG 813)

## Ascribed to RUISDAEL

P197

### P197    LANDSCAPE WITH A FARM

Inscribed: . . .*R* (monogram?)

Canvas 47·0 × 57·8

Probably painted in Haarlem *c.* 1650, but weaknesses in the execution suggest P197 is not by Ruisdael himself. (HdG 662 as Ruisdael, the figures and cattle attributed to A. van de Velde)

Purchased by the 4th Marquess of Hertford 1861

## After RUISDAEL

P148

### P148    WILD DUCK SHOOTING

Inscribed: *JVRuisdael*

Canvas 31·1 × 26·7

The costumes suggest a date in the later 17th century. (HdG 559, 620a)

Acquired by 1872

**P247   SUNSET IN A WOOD**

Inscribed: *JVRuisdael*

Canvas 90·8 × 78·1

The concept of this landscape would appear to date from after the 17th century. (HdG 1033)

Acquired by 1872

P247

## Gabriel de SAINT-AUBIN
### 1724–1780

b. and d. Paris; the most talented of a family of artists, pupil of Jeurat, de Vermont and Boucher, q.v.; engraver and draughtsman, an indefatigable illustrator of Parisian life.

**P780 (formerly M296)   A FÊTE IN THE COLISÉE, PARIS**

Signed: *G. d. St. A 1772* and *Colisée dessiné sur le lieu par Gabriel de St. Aubin 1772*

Gouache on paper 16·3 × 22·2

The subject is said to have been an entertainment given by Louis XV in 1772. The Colisée was established in 1770, north of the Champs-Élysées; it was a pleasure dome in imitation of Vauxhall Gardens in London.

Aquired after 1860

## Simon SAINT-JEAN
### 1808–1860

b. Lyon, d. Ecully; pupil of Révoil and Lepage at Lyon; a flower-painter, greatly influenced by van Huijsum, q.v.

P569

**P569   FLOWERS AND FRUIT**
Signed: *St. Jean*
Canvas 89·5 × 72·4
Acquired by 1872

P601

**P601   FLOWERS AND FRUIT**
Signed: *Saint Jean 1853*
Canvas 44·5 × 54·0
Acquired by 1872

P760

**P760   FLOWERS AND GRAPES**
Signed: *St. Jean 1846*
Canvas 125·4 × 102·2
Acquired by 1872

**P761    FLOWERS AND GRAPES**

Signed: *St. Jean 1844*

Canvas 124·8 × 101·0

Acquired by 1872

P761

## James SANT

### 1820–1916

b. Croydon, d. London; pupil of J. Varley and Callcott; Principal Painter in Ordinary to Queen Victoria 1871; painted portraits and genre scenes.

**P602    A LADY WITH FLOWERS**

Canvas 76·2 × 63·2

The painter stated that the model was his sister, Julia, possibly indicating a date *c.* 1850.

Acquired by 1872

P602

# Andrea del SARTO (Andrea d'Agnolo)
## 1486–1530

b. and d. Florence; the most important painter working in Florence while Raphael and Michelangelo were working in Rome; apart from a visit to Paris in 1518–19 he stayed in Florence. (S. J. Freedberg, *Andrea del Sarto*, Harvard, 1963; J. Shearman, *Andrea del Sarto*, 1965)

P9

### P9  VIRGIN AND CHILD WITH ST JOHN THE BAPTIST AND TWO ANGELS

Signed: ANDREA DEL SARTO FLORENTINO FACIEBAT and AA (monogram)

Panel 109·2 × 83·8

In the right distance St Anthony of Padua kneels before the music-making angel in the sky. Painted *c.* 1517–19. Preliminary drawings are in the British Museum and the Louvre; more than twenty copies of the composition have been recorded. (Freedberg 43; Shearman 48)

Purchased by the 4th Marquess of Hertford 1850

# SASSOFERRATO (Giovanni Battista Salvi)
## 1609–1685

b. Sassoferrato, d. Florence or Rome; influenced by Domenichino, q.v., and the Bolognese academicians; worked in Rome and Umbria.

P126

### P126  VIRGIN AND CHILD

Canvas 47·3 × 44·1

The composition is repeated in P565, q.v.

Purchased by the 4th Marquess of Hertford 1849

## P565 VIRGIN AND CHILD

Canvas 86·0 × 73·3

Similar to P126, q.v., this composition was repeated many times by the artist and his assistants.

Acquired by 1872

P565

## P646 THE MYSTIC MARRIAGE OF ST CATHERINE

Canvas 233·4 × 138·1

The subject refers to the dream of St Catherine of Alexandria in which, after her baptism, Christ took her as his celestial spouse; see also Dolci P562, and Cima P1. A drawing for the whole composition is at Windsor.

Purchased by the 4th Marquess of Hertford 1856

P646

# Godfried SCHALCKEN
## 1643–1706

b. Made, near Dordrecht, d. The Hague; pupil of Dou, q.v.; worked in Dordrecht and The Hague; visited London 1692–97 and probably Düsseldorf c. 1703; specialised in candle-lit genre scenes, also painted portraits.

P171

**P171    A GIRL THREADING A NEEDLE BY CANDLELIGHT**

Signed: *G. Schalcken*

Panel 20·3 × 16·5

(HdG 195).

Purchased by the 3rd Marquess of Hertford 1807

# Ary SCHEFFER
## 1795–1858

b. Dordrecht, d. Argenteuil; pupil of his father in Holland, and of Guérin in Paris; portrait and history painter.

P284

**P284    MARGARET AT THE WELL**

Signed: *Ary Scheffer 1858*

Canvas 162·9 × 102·9

The subject is taken from Goethe's *Faust* i (Margaret and Lisbeth: 'now the reproach and sin are mine').

Purchased by Sir Richard Wallace 1872

## P298    PORTRAIT OF A CHILD

Signed: *EI. AS 1829* (i.e. E. Isabey and A.
Scheffer, see below)

Canvas 42·9 × 29·2

Painted in collaboration with Eugène Isabey,
q.v.

Acquired by 1872

P298

## P316    FRANCESCA DA RIMINI

Signed: *Ary Scheffer 1835*

Canvas 169·5 × 238·1

The subject is taken from Dante's *Inferno* v:
Paolo and Francesca 'hand in hand on the
dark wind drifting go'. Set in a carved frame,
probably devised by the artist, bearing quo-
tations from Dante. P316 was repaired by
Scheffer in 1853. A repetition, in a similar
frame, is in the Repin Institute, Leningrad; of
several further versions, one is in the Louvre.
Sketches for the composition are in the Scheffer
Museum, Dordrecht, and the Musée Bargoin,
Clermont-Ferrand.

Purchased by the 4th Marquess of Hertford
1870

P316

P321

**P321   THE RETURN OF THE PRODIGAL SON**

Signed: *Ary Scheffer 18*[5?]*7*

Panel 61·0 × 49·8

The subject is taken from *Luke* xv, 11–21. A preliminary study is in the Scheffer Museum, Dordrecht.

Acquired by 1872

P616

**P616   THE SISTER OF MERCY**

Signed: *A. Scheffer*

Panel 32·4 × 40·6

Painted in 1829.

Acquired by 1872

P687

**P687   A MOTHER AND CHILD**

Signed: *A. Scheffer*

Water-colour 20·6 × 15·6

Acquired by 1874

# Andreas SCHELFHOUT
## 1787–1870

b. and d. The Hague; pupil of Breckenheimer.

### P573 WINTER IN HOLLAND

Signed: *A. Schelfhout f. 1843*

Panel 46·4 × 62·9

Apparently influenced by Aert van der Neer, q.v.

Acquired by 1872

P573

# Frédéric-Henri SCHOPIN
## 1804–1880

b. Lübeck, d. Montigny-sur-Loing; pupil of Gros, q.v. and the École des Beaux-Arts; history and portrait painter.

### P568 THE DIVORCE OF THE EMPRESS JOSEPHINE

Signed: *H. Schopin 1846*

Canvas 56·5 × 81·3

The Empress (see Prud'hon P315), with her daughter Hortense de Beauharnais (1783–1837) by her side, has just signed the act of separation; Prince Eugène de Beauharnais (1781–1824), her son, stands by Napoleon. The divorce took place in 1809. Exhibited in the Salon of 1847 with a quotation from Marco de Saint-Hilaire in the catalogue.

Purchased by the 4th Marquess of Hertford 1865

P568

# Frans SNIJDERS
## 1579–1657

b. and d. Antwerp; pupil of P. Brueghel II and H. van Balen I in Antwerp; travelled in Italy 1608–9; an accomplished painter of still-life, he sometimes collaborated with other artists, notably Rubens, q.v.; see also Jordaens, P120.

### P72   DEAD GAME WITH MALE FIGURE

Canvas 128·3 × 200·7

The number 327 appears in red on the canvas.

Acquired by 1872

P72

# Lo SPAGNA
## active 1504 died 1528

d. Spoleto; Giovanni di Pietro, a Spaniard, known as Lo Spagna; worked in Perugia, Todi, Spoleto etc.; influenced by Perugino and Raphael.

P545

### P545   THE ASSUMPTION OF ST MARY MAGDALENE

Paper on panel 37·1 × 29·5

Listed by Berenson as St Mary of Egypt.

# (William) Clarkson STANFIELD
## 1793–1867

b. Sunderland, d. London; served at sea 1808–16; scenery painter in London before becoming an accomplished land- and seascape painter; his work was influenced by Bonington, q.v. and Turner, q.v.; see also Bonington P727.

### P343   BEILSTEIN ON THE MOSELLE

Canvas 117·8 × 166·1

Exhibited at the RA in 1837.

Purchased by the 4th Marquess of Hertford 1863

P343

### P354   ORFORD ON THE RIVER ORE, SUFFOLK

Signed: *C. Stanfield 1833*

Panel 25·4 × 30·5

Sudbourn Hall, the country seat of Sir Richard Wallace, was near Orford which was a Hertford family borough.

Purchased by Sir Richard Wallace 1875

P354

### P667   A CANAL IN VENICE

Inscribed: *Venice Oct. 25th 1830*

Water-colour 34·0 × 23·5

Acquired by 1874

P667

**P712   SAN GIORGIO MAGGIORE, VENICE**

Signed: *CS*

Water-colour 19·7 × 26·0

Acquired by 1874

P712

# Jan STEEN
## 1625/6–1679

b. and d. Leiden; pupil of Knüpfer in Utrecht, Adriaen van Ostade, q.v., in Haarlem, and van Goyen in The Hague; settled in Haarlem by 1661 and moved to Leiden in 1670; painter of lively genre scenes and some religious subjects.

**P111   THE CHRISTENING FEAST**

Signed: *J. Steen 1664*

Canvas 88·9 × 108·6

(HdG 448)

Acquired by 1872

P111

**P150   THE LUTE PLAYER**

Signed: *JStee. .*

Canvas 38·1 × 52·1 enlarged to 40·6 × 52·1

Painted in the late 1660s or early 1670s. Cleaned and restored 1977 when overpainting in the central area was removed, re-emphasising that this is a brothel scene. The man with the pipe is possibly the artist. (HdG 411, 437)

Acquired by 1872

P150

## P154 THE HARPSICHORD LESSON

Signed: *J. Steen*

Panel 36·5 × 48·3

P154

The picture on the wall of *Venus and Cupid* provides the key to the subject (which has been justly equated with Shakespeare's 128th Sonnet). The harpsichord is inscribed *Sol. De. Gloria* (to God alone the Glory). The composition may have inspired Fragonard's *La leçon de musique* (Louvre). Probably painted in the early 1660s. (HdG 412)

Purchased by the 4th Marquess of Hertford 1859

## P158 MERRYMAKING IN A TAVERN

Signed: *JS*

Canvas 74·3 × 67·3

Cleaned in 1976. Probably painted in the early 1670s; Steen kept an inn in Leiden in the 1670s. (HdG 599)

Acquired by 1872

P158

## P209 THE VILLAGE ALCHEMIST

Signed: *J. Steen*

Panel 41·6 × 29·8

One of the men holds a sheet inscribed *Para*[celsus], the celebrated 16th-century alchemist. Probably painted in 1668; engraved by Boydell as *The Dutch Chymist*. (HdG 228)

Acquired by the 3rd Marquess of Hertford by 1833

P209

# Jacobus STORCK, attributed to
## 1641–after 1693

Probably b. and d. Amsterdam; brother of Abraham and Johannes, also marine painters in that city.

P208

### P208   CASTLE ON A RIVER IN HOLLAND

Signed: *I. Storck*

Canvas 94·0 × 119·1

The topography is probably fanciful. A similar composition (London art market 1967) signed *Jacobus Storck*, suggests that he, rather than his brother Johannes (as previously suggested), painted P208.

Purchased by Sir Richard Wallace 1877

# Jacob van STRIJ, attributed to
## 1756–1815

b. and d. Dordrecht; pupil of A. C. Lens; with his brother, Abraham, produced many landscapes with cattle in the manner of Cuyp, q.v.; see also Cuyp, After, P250, P253, P255.

P147

### P147   CATTLE

Panel 40·6 × 37·8

Acquired by 1872

# Thomas SULLY
## 1783–1872

b. Horncastle, Lincs., d. Philadelphia; settled in South Carolina 1792 and in Philadelphia 1808; came to London 1809 to study under West and Lawrence, q.v., and again in 1837–38, see below.

### P564 QUEEN VICTORIA

Signed: *TS June 1838 London*

Canvas 141·0 × 113·0

For the sitter, and a related drawing, see Denning P765; her coronation took place on 28 June 1838. P564, together with a head and shoulders study (Metropolitan Museum, New York), was a preliminary version of a whole-length portrait commissioned by the Society of the Sons of St George, Philadelphia, which Sully completed in 1839 (still with the Society). P564 became the basis for an engraving by C. Wagstaff, published by Hodgson and Graves in 1838. Many versions and derivations of the whole-length exist, including a replica by Sully (St Andrews Society, Charleston, South Carolina).

Purchased by the 4th Marquess of Hertford 1855

P564

# William Robert SYMONDS
## 1851–1934

b. Yoxford, Suffolk; studied in London and Antwerp; settled in London 1861.

### P578 SIR RICHARD WALLACE

Signed: *W.R. Symonds 1885*

Canvas 67·6 × 56·2

Richard Wallace (1818–90), illegitimate son of the 4th Marquess of Hertford, m. 1871 Julie Castelnau; cr. Baronet 1871; Hertford House and Sudbourn Hall, Suffolk, were his principal English residences; his widow bequeathed The Wallace Collection to the Nation in 1897. P578 was exhibited at the RA in 1885.

Presented to Sir Richard and Lady Wallace by Tenants and Friends of the Sudbourn Estate 1885

P578

# David TENIERS the younger
## 1610–1690

b. Antwerp, d. Brussels; pupil of his father, David I; official painter and *ayuda de camera* to the Archduke Leopold-Wilhelm, Governor of the Netherlands 1646–56, and his successor, Don Juan of Austria, Governor 1656–59, in Brussels; helped establish the Académie Royale in Antwerp 1662; landscape and genre painter.

P191

### P191    A "JOYEUSE ENTRÉE"

Signed: D. TENIERS F.

Canvas 66·7 × 83·2

P191 possibly shows the entry of Don Juan José of Austria (1629–79), illegitimate son of Philip IV of Spain), into Antwerp as Governor of the Netherlands in 1656. Its decorative border may indicate that it was intended as a tapestry design. Three other pictures, apparently *en suite* with P191 (sold in Paris in 1903), show an embarkation, a naval engagement against Turkish forces, and an arrival by sea (this now in the Louvre); the first two may refer to the earlier Don Juan's victory at Lepanto in 1571, since neither of the Governors for whom Teniers worked in Brussels was engaged in conspicuous naval operations.

Purchased by Sir Richard Wallace 1872

P196

### P196    A RIVERSIDE INN

Signed: D. TENIERS *f.*

Panel 24·8 × 35·2

Acquired by 1872

P210

### P210    THE DELIVERANCE OF ST PETER

Signed: D. TENIERS *f.*

Copper 36·2 × 49·8

The biblical subject (right background) is taken from *Acts* xii, 6–10.

Acquired by 1872

## P227 BOORS CAROUSING

Signed: DAVID TENIERS *f*.: the print on the wall dated *1644*

Copper 36·5 × 49·8

Purchased by the 4th Marquess of Hertford 1858

P227

## P231 GAMBLING SCENE AT AN INN

Signed: DAVID TENIERS *fec*.

Panel 40·9 × 56·5

Acquired by 1872

P231

**P635–638** below are four of the 244 small copies Teniers made from the Italian pictures in the collection of the Archduke Leopold-Wilhelm at the Château de Coudenberg, Brussels, between 1647 and 1656. Teniers was *ayuda de camera* (curator) for the Archduke and his copies were made preparatory for engravings, published in 1660 as Teniers's *Theatrum Pictoricum*. The Archduke's collection returned in 1656 from Brussels to Vienna, where many of the pictures became part of the Imperial collection, and hence the Kunsthistorisches Museum.

## P635 THE ASCENSION after Leandro Bassano

Panel 31·1 × 21·6

Engraved by I. Troyen; the original is in the Musée de l'Art Ancien, Brussels.

P635

P636

### P636   THE VIRGIN OF THE CHERRIES
**after Titian**

Canvas on panel 14·3 × 17·1

Engraved by L. Vorsterman; the original is in the Kunsthistorisches Museum, Vienna.

P637

### P637   THE WOMAN TAKEN IN ADULTERY after Titian

Panel 17·1 × 22·5

Engraved by I. Troyen; the original is in the Kunsthistorisches Museum, Vienna.

Acquired by 1872

P638

### P638   THE MYSTIC MARRIAGE OF ST CATHERINE after Fetti

Panel 31·1 × 21·6

Engraved by P. Lisebetius; the original is in the Kunsthistorisches Museum, Vienna.

# TITIAN

*c.* 1485–1576

b. Pieve di Cadore, d. Venice; Tiziano Vecelli, anglicised as Titian; pupil of Giovanni Bellini in Venice and influenced by Giorgione; worked nearly all his long life in Venice. See also Teniers P636 and P637, and Robert Fleury P361. (H. Wethey, *Titian*, vol. 3, 1975)

### P11   PERSEUS AND ANDROMEDA

Canvas 182·9 × 198·8

The subject is taken from Ovid, *Metamorphoses*, iv: Andromeda, about to be sacrificed to a sea-monster sent by Neptune, because her mother had claimed her daughter was more beautiful than the Nereides (the sea-nymphs), is rescued by Perseus; see also Lemoyne P417. Painted probably 1554–56 for Philip II of Spain, one of the great *poesie* Titian painted for him in his full maturity (see also P5 below). X-rays reveal considerable changes in the composition (there was a whole-length figure to the right). Two early copies are in the Prado, Madrid, and the Hermitage, Leningrad. P11 was once in the collection of van Dyck, q.v. (Wethey 30)

Purchased by the 3rd Marquess of Hertford 1815

P11

## Follower of TITIAN

**P19 CUPID WOUNDED, COMPLAINS TO VENUS (L'Amour piqué)**

Canvas 111·8 × 139·7

Probably painted *c.* 1520 and evidently influenced by Titian without attaining the master's quality. Called Giorgione when in the Orleans collection. A copy is in a private collection in Italy. A drawing by van Dyck, q.v., in his Italian Sketchbook (British Museum) copies the figure composition from P19. (Wethey X-44)

Purchased by the 4th Marquess of Hertford 1859

P19

# After TITIAN

P5

## P5   THE RAPE OF EUROPA

Canvas 59·1 × 72·4

For the subject, see Boucher P484. A reduced copy of uncertain date of the picture now in the Isabella Stewart Gardner Museum, Boston (which was in Spain in the 17th century, France in the 18th, and England in the 19th). (Wethey 32 copy 3)

Purchased by the 4th Marquess of Hertford 1857

P546

## P546   DANAE AND THE GOLDEN RAIN

Canvas 32·1 × 44·8

The subject is taken from Ovid's *Metamorphoses*, iv. A reduced copy, possibly 18th century, of the picture now in the Museo di Capodimonte, Naples. (Wethey 5 copy 8)

Purchased by the 4th Marquess of Hertford 1856

# François de TROY, attributed to
## 1645–1730

b. Toulouse, d. Paris; pupil of his father and of Claude Loir; early history subjects were succeeded by portraits admired by Louis XIV and Mesdames Montespan and Maintenon; Director of the Académie 1708; father of J-F. de Troy, q.v.

## P122   LOUIS XIV AND HIS HEIRS

Canvas 129·2 × 162·2

From the left: Charlotte, duchesse de Ventadour (1661–1744), governess of the Royal children from 1709; Louis, 2nd duc de Bretagne (1707–12) eldest surviving son of the duc de Bourgogne; Louis, *Le grand dauphin*, (1661–1711), son of Louis XIV; Louis XIV (1643–1715); Louis, duc de Bourgogne (1682–1712), eldest son of *le grand dauphin*. Busts of Henri IV (left) and Louis XIII complete the representation of the male line of the ruling House of Bourbon.

Almost certainly commissioned by the duchesse de Ventadour, probably in 1709 to mark her appointment as governess; her mourning dress would be for her mother (the maréchale de la Mothe) whom she had succeeded in the office.

Attributed to de Troy in the 18th century, exhibited as Largillierre in 1783; known as Largillierre until 1939 when listed as de Troy by Vollmer, an attribution supported by Cailleux in 1971.

Acquired by 1872

P122

# Jean-François de TROY
## 1679–1752

b. Paris, d. Rome; pupil of his father François, q.v.; and at the Académie; in Italy c. 1699–1706; Director of the French school at Rome 1738–52; painter of histories and *fêtes galantes*.

### P463   A HUNT BREAKFAST

Signed: DE TROY 1737

Canvas 55·9 × 45·7

With P470 below, a sketch for a picture commissioned by Louis XV for the dining room of the *petits appartements* at Fontainebleau. The finished pictures were exhibited at the Salon in 1737; the *Hunt Breakfast* (238 × 168) is in a Swiss private collection.

Purchased by Sir Richard Wallace 1872

P463

P470

### P470   THE DEATH OF A STAG

Signed: DE TROY 1737

Canvas 55·2 × 45·7

See P463 above. The finished version is now untraced.

Purchased by Sir Richard Wallace 1872

## Constant TROYON
### 1810–1865

b. Sèvres, d. Paris; studied as a flower-painter in the Sèvres factory under Riocreux but, encouraged by Roqueplan, q.v., turned to landscape subjects; settled in Paris 1842; one of the Barbizon school.

### P344   WATERING CATTLE

Signed: *C. Troyon*

Canvas 123·8 × 163·8

Probably painted *c.* 1860.

Acquired by 1872

P344

P359

### P359   CATTLE IN STORMY WEATHER

Signed: *C. Troyon 1857*

Panel 40·6 × 58·4

Acquired by 1872

# Joseph Mallord William TURNER
## 1775–1851

b. and d. London; studied at the RA schools; his early work was influenced by J. R. Cozens and Girtin; his extraordinary landscape vision was also developed by frequent European visits from 1802 onwards.

### P651  WOODCOCK-SHOOTING ON THE CHEVIN, YORKSHIRE

Signed: *J M W Turner R.A. 1813*

Water-colour 27·9 × 39·7

Together with P654, P661 and P664 below, P651 was commissioned by Sir Henry Pilkington, who is said to be the sportsman in the foreground.

Purchased by the 4th Marquess of Hertford 1863

P651

### P654  SCARBOROUGH CASTLE: BOYS CRAB-FISHING

Signed: *J W Turner, R.A. 1809*

Water-colour 27·9 × 39·4

A favourite subject with Turner, P654 was possibly exhibited at the RA in 1811 as *Scarborough Town and Castle: Morning: Boys collecting Crabs.* See P651.

Purchased by the 4th Marquess of Hertford 1863

P654

### P661  MOWBRAY LODGE, RIPON, YORKSHIRE

Signed: *. . .M. Turner, R.A.*

Water-colour 27·9 × 39·4

Probably painted *c.* 1813. See P651.

Purchased by the 4th Marquess of Hertford 1863

P661

### P664  GROUSE-SHOOTING

Signed: *J M W Turner RA. PP* (i.e. Professor of Perspective)

Water-colour 27·9 × 39·4

Probably painted *c.* 1813; Turner was made Professor of Perspective in 1807. See P651.

Purchased by the 4th Marquess of Hertford 1863

P664

# UMBRIAN SCHOOL
late 15th–early 16th century

P540

### P540   THE VIRGIN

Fresco 59·7 × 57·8

Evidently a fragment from an Annunciation.

# Diego VELAZQUEZ
1599–1660

b. Seville, d. Madrid; pupil of F. Pacheco in Seville; moved to Madrid 1623 and made Court Painter to Philip IV the same year; visited Italy 1629–31 and 1649–51; he employed many assistants to judge by the number of contemporary versions of his official portraits.

P12

### P12   DON BALTASAR CARLOS IN INFANCY

Canvas 119·4 × 97·8

The sitter (1629–44) was the eldest son of Philip IV and of his first wife, Isabella of Bourbon; see also P4 and P6 below. Painted *c.* 1632 but possibly left unfinished by Velazquez, the background being inferior in execution. Engraved by J. Gauchard before 1870, showing the tasselled curtains removed in cleaning in 1938.

Purchased by the 4th Marquess of Hertford 1853

## P88   LADY WITH A FAN

Canvas 94·6 × 69·8

Probably painted 1638–39; a royal edict of 1639 forbade both the veiling of the face and the low-necked bodice. Cleaned and restored 1975 when the complete fan was revealed, together with the silver pendant below the bow (engravings show that this was painted over between 1812 and 1839). Thoré, writing in 1857, considered that 'There is no other painting that better represents both Spain and Velazquez'. (E. Harris, *Burlington Magazine*, May 1975, pp. 316–19)

Purchased by the 4th Marquess of Hertford 1847

P88

# After VELAZQUEZ

## P4   DON BALTASAR CARLOS

Canvas 154·3 × 109·2

For the sitter see P12 above and P6 below. A copy of the portrait painted *c*. 1639 now in the Kunsthistorisches Museum, Vienna. P4 once belonged to Joshua Reynolds, q.v., who 're-paired' it.

Purchased by the 4th Marquess of Hertford 1848

P4

P6

## P6   DON BALTASAR CARLOS IN THE RIDING SCHOOL

Canvas 132·7 × 103·2

For the sitter see P12 above, and P4 above. The setting is the Palace of Buen Retiro, near Madrid, and the Prince is about to practise tilting. Probably painted between *c.* 1644 and 1646, P6 is a lively but inferior version of the painting now belonging to the Grosvenor Estate (144 × 91, *c.* 1636) without the figures of the Conde-Duque de Olivares (banished from the Court 1643, see P109 below) and Queen Isabella (d. 1644). Possibly painted by J. B. del Mazo (*c.* 1612/16–67), the pupil of Velazquez who became the Prince's Painter. (E. Harris, *Burlington Magazine*, May 1976, pp. 266–74)

Purchased by the 4th Marquess of Hertford 1856

P70

## P70   PHILIP IV HUNTING THE WILD BOAR

Canvas 69·8 × 111·1

Philip IV (1605–63) came to the Spanish throne in 1621. Copy of the picture in the National Gallery, (no. 197, *c.* 182 × 302) but lacking many of the figures.

Purchased by the 4th Marquess of Hertford 1859

P100

## P100   THE INFANTA MARGARITA

Canvas 71·8 × 56·8

Margarita (1651–73), daughter of Philip IV, see P70 above, m. 1666 the Emperor Leopold I, her mother's brother. P100 derives from the whole-length Velazquez pattern of *c.* 1656 of which there are examples in the Staedelsches Kunstinstitut, Frankfurt, and in the Kunsthistorisches Museum, Vienna.

Acquired by 1872

## P106   PHILIP IV ON HORSEBACK

Canvas 67·6 × 59·7

For the sitter see P70 above. Copy of the painting in the Prado, Madrid (no. 1178, 301 × 314, c. 1635). See P109 below.

Purchased by Sir Richard Wallace 1872

P106

## P109   THE CONDE-DUQUE DE OLIVARES ON HORSEBACK

Canvas 67·9 × 59·7

Olivares (1587–1645) was Philip IV's most influential prime minister until he was exiled, at the Queen's insistence, in 1643. Copy, possibly 19th century, of the painting in the Prado, Madrid (no. 1181, 313 × 239, c. 1631–35; perhaps intended as a pendant to P106 above.

Purchased by Sir Richard Wallace 1872

P109

# Adriaen van de VELDE
## 1636–1672

b. and d. Amsterdam; son of the marine painter Willem I, brother of Willem II, q.v.; pupil of his father and J. Wijnants, q.v., in Haarlem; settled in Amsterdam by 1657; painter of animals and landscapes, and of figures for others (see Hackaert, van der Heyden, Ruisdael, W. van de Velde and Wijnants).

### P80   THE MIGRATION OF JACOB

Signed: *A.V. Velde f. 1663*

Canvas 135·9 × 181·0

The subject is taken from *Genesis* xxxii, 22–4: Jacob sends his family across the gorge of Jabbok as he goes to meet Esau. (HdG 2)

Purchased by the 4th Marquess of Hertford 1845

P80

P199

### P199   NOONDAY REST

Signed: *A.V. Velde f. 1663*

Panel 32·4 × 42·9

(HdG 218)

Purchased by the 4th Marquess of Hertford 1867

# Willem van de VELDE the younger
## 1633–1707

b. Leiden, d. London; pupil of his father, Willem I, and S. de Vlieger; lived in Amsterdam until moving to London 1673 where with his father he entered the service of Charles II as a painter of sea battles.

**P77    THE BATTLE OF
SCHEVENINGEN**

Signed: *W.V.V.*

Canvas 89·9 × 109·5

The battle (named after the Dutch coast town now on the outskirts of The Hague) was fought in 1653 between the English, under General Monck, and the Dutch, under Admiral Marten Tromp; it resulted in a decisive English victory and the death of Tromp (whose flagship appears in the left background). Probably painted *c.* 1653; a grisaille of the battle by Willem I is in the National Maritime Museum. (HdG 64)

P77

Acquired by 1872

**P137    A DUTCH MAN-OF-WAR
SALUTING**

Signed: *W.V. Velde*

Canvas 172·7 × 235·6

(HdG 89)

Purchased by the 4th Marquess of Hertford 1846

P137

P143

### P143   BOATS AT LOW WATER

Signed: *W.V.V.*

Canvas 33·3 × 37·5

(HdG 326)

Purchased by the 4th Marquess of Hertford 1861

P145

### P145   SHIPS IN A CALM

Signed: *W.V. Velde*

Canvas 32·7 × 36·5

(HdG 209)

Acquired by 1872

P194

### P194   THE EMBARKATION OF CHARLES II AT SCHEVENINGEN

Signed: *W.V.V.*

Canvas 49·5 × 58·4

The exiled Charles embarked at Scheveningen on 23 May 1660 to cross to Dover and revive the English monarchy after the Commonwealth interregnum. Two drawings relating to P194 are in the National Maritime Museum and in the National Gallery of Scotland. The figures in P194 have been attributed to A. van de Velde, q.v., the artist's brother. (HdG 50)

Acquired by 1872

P215

### P215   SHIPS IN A BREEZE

Signed: *W.V.V.*

Panel 41·6 × 55·2

(HdG 494)

Purchased by the 4th Marquess of Hertford 1845

**P221   A COAST SCENE WITH SHIPPING**

Signed: *W.V. Velde 1675*

Panel 38·1 × 49·2

(HdG 210)

Purchased by the 4th Marquess of Hertford 1857

P221

**P246   LANDING FROM SHIPS OF WAR**

Signed: *W.V. Velde*

Canvas 62·2 × 75·9

The saluting ship is probably Cornelis van Tromp's flagship, the *Gouden Leeuw* (the Golden Lion); the successful Dutch Admiral was the second son of Admiral Marten Tromp, see P77 above. (HdG 90)

Acquired by 1872

P246

# VENETIAN SCHOOL
18th century

**P498   THE GRAND CANAL WITH SAN SIMEONE PICCOLO**

Canvas 94·3 × 145·4

Looking north-east from San Simeone Piccolo towards the entrance to the Canareggio with the campanile of S. Geremia in the distance. (Constable, *Canaletto*, 261 as school of Canaletto)

Acquired by the 4th Marquess of Hertford by 1859

P498

P513

### P513  THE BUCENTAUR SETTING OUT

Canvas 54·0 × 83·2

Every Ascension Day the *Bucentaur* carried the Doge to the Lido where he celebrated the marriage of Venice with the Adriatic by casting a ring into the sea. P513 derives from an engraving by G. B. Brustolon, after a drawing by Canaletto, part of a set of the twelve *Solennità Dogali* (see also Canaletto and studio P500) (Constable, *Canaletto*, 330 v 4a, as school of Canaletto)

Acquired by 1872

# Eugène-Joseph VERBOECKHOVEN
## 1799–1881

b. Warneton, d. Brussels; pupil of his father, Barthélémy; animal and landscape painter in the Dutch 17th-century tradition.

P622

### P622  SHEEP AND COWS

Signed: *Eugene Verboeckhoven f. 1844*

Panel 40·6 × 56·5

Acquired by 1872

# Claude-Joseph VERNET
## 1714–1789

b. Avignon, d. Paris; studied under his father, Antoine, and at Aix under J. Viali; worked in Rome 1734–52, settled in Paris 1753; influenced by Manglard, painter of romantic seascapes and coastal topography.

### P135  A STORM WITH A SHIPWRECK

Signed: *J. Vernet f. 1754*

Canvas 87·9 × 138·1

Painted for the marquis de Marigny, *directeur des bâtiments* and brother of Mme. de Pompadour (see Boucher P418), who obtained for Vernet the commission to paint the ports of France. Exhibited in the Salon of 1755.

Acquired by 1872

P135

## P480   A RIVER SCENE

Signed: *J. Vernet*

Canvas 65·7 × 97·5

Probably painted *c.* 1780, according to Ingersoll-Smouse.

Purchased by the 4th Marquess of Hertford 1855

P480

# Émile-Jean-Horace VERNET
## 1789–1863

b. and d. Paris; grandson of C-J. Vernet, q.v.; pupil of his father, Carle, and his mother's father, Moreau le jeune; Director of the Académie at Rome 1828–35; painted many battle-pieces for King Louis-Philippe at Versailles, a friend of the 4th Marquess of Hertford.

## P277   A ROMAN HERDSMAN DRIVING CATTLE

Signed: *H. Vernet Rome 1829*

Canvas 88·9 × 133·3

Acquired by the 4th Marquess of Hertford by 1857.

P277

**P280    THE ARAB TALE-TELLER**

Signed: *Horace Vernet Rome 1833*

Canvas 100·3 × 137·8

Commissioned by the 12th Earl of Pembroke. A comparable subject, *Le parlementaire*, sd 1834, is at Chantilly.

Acquired by the 4th Marquess of Hertford by 1857

P280

P336

**P336    AN EASTERN TRADER**

Signed: *HV*

Canvas 27·3 × 20·3

## P346    JUDAH AND TAMAR

Signed: *H$^{ce}$ Vernet Malte 1840*

Canvas 129·5 × 98·1

The subject is taken from *Genesis* xxxviii, 13–19: Tamar seduces her father-in-law, Judah. Exhibited in the Salon of 1843. A version (71 × 58) is in the Musée Magnin, Dijon.

Purchased by the 4th Marquess of Hertford 1865

P346

## P349    JOSEPH'S COAT

Signed: *H$^{ce}$ Vernet Afrique 1853*

Canvas 139·7 × 104·1

The subject is taken from *Genesis* xxxvii, 31–33.

Purchased by the 4th Marquess of Hertford 1866

P349

## P367    A SENTINEL

Signed: *H. Vernet*

Canvas 65·4 × 55·2

Engraved by Jazet (?J. P. M. Jazet, 1788–1871).

P367

P368

### P368   CONRAD, THE CORSAIR

Signed: *H. Vernet 1824*

Canvas 65·4 × 54·0

The subject is taken from Byron's *The Corsair*, 1814, canto i, verse 6 (see also Bonington P749).

Acquired by 1872

P572

### P572   NAPOLEON REVIEWING THE IMPERIAL GUARD

Signed: *HV*

Canvas 63·2 × 94·9

At the Tuileries, with the Arc du Carrousel to the right. Probably painted *c.* 1838, as a study for the picture of this title commissioned by the Tsar Nicholas I and delivered in July 1838.

Purchased by the 4th Marquess of Hertford 1857

P575

### P575   THE APOTHEOSIS OF NAPOLEON

Signed: *H. Vernet 1821*

Canvas 54·6 × 81·3

For Napoleon, see Gros P303. Painted in the year of his death, the floating plank inscribed with the names of ten of his battles, the last *Wat*[erloo]

Acquired by 1872

P577

### P577   THE BRIGAND BETRAYED

Signed: *H. Vernet*

Canvas 54·9 × 66·0

Acquired by 1872

**P582 THE VETERAN AT HOME**

Signed: *H. Vernet 1823*

Canvas 46·4 × 38·1

Acquired by 1872

P582

**P584 ARABS TRAVELLING IN THE DESERT**

Signed: *H. Vernet 1843*

Canvas 47·3 × 58·4

Exhibited in the Salon of 1844.

Acquired by 1872

P584

**P585 THE LION HUNT**

Signed: *H. Vernet 1836*

Canvas 57·2 × 81·6

A larger version (138 × 168) is in a private collection, St Louis, Missouri.

Acquired by 1872

P585

**P593 A BASHI-BAZOUK**

Signed: *H. Vernet 1860*

Canvas 55·9 × 47·0

An irregular member of the Turkish army.

Purchased by the 4th Marquess of Hertford 1863

P593

P598

**P598   PEACE AND WAR**

Signed: *Horace Vernet 1820*

Canvas 55·2 × 46·4

When sold from the La Rochefoucault-
Liancourt collection in 1827 P598 was de-
scribed as having been inspired by Virgil's
*Georgics* i, 493–8.

Acquired by 1872

P606

**P606   ALLAN MACAULAY**

Signed: *H. Vernet 1823*

Canvas 65·4 × 54·9

The subject is taken from Scott's *Legend of
Montrose*, 1819. Exhibited in the Salon of 1824.

Acquired by 1872

P607

**P607   THE DOG OF THE REGIMENT
WOUNDED**

Signed: *H. Vernet 1819*

Canvas 54·6 × 65·4

Acquired by 1872

P608

**P608   THE SPORTSMAN**

Signed: *H. Vernet 1824*

Canvas 47·6 × 61·0

Exhibited in the Salon of 1824.

Acquired by 1872

**P610    A LADY HAWKING**

Signed: *H. Vernet 1839*

Canvas 69·5 × 49·5

Acquired by 1872

P610

**P613    THE DEAD TRUMPETER**

Signed: *H. Vernet 1819*

Canvas 54·6 × 65·4

Acquired by 1872

P613

**P614    THE QUARRY**

Signed: *H. Vernet 1823*

Canvas 47·6 × 61·6

Exhibited in the Salon of 1824.

Acquired by 1872

P614

**P619    THE DUKE OF NEMOURS
        ENTERING CONSTANTINE**

Signed: *H. Vernet*

Zinc 27·0 × 20·0

The duc de Nemours (1814–96), 2nd son of
King Louis-Philippe, captured Constantine in
north-east Algeria on 15th October 1837.

Acquired by 1872

P619

P719

**P719    A CHARGE OF CUIRASSIERS**
Signed: *H. Vernet 1823*
Water-colour 23·5 × 31·7
Acquired by 1874

P724

**P724    HERON-SHOOTING**
Signed: *H. Vernet*
Sepia drawing 20·0 × 26·4
Acquired by 1872

P728

**P728    ON THE MARCH**
Signed: *H. Vernet 1823*
Water-colour 19·7 × 13·3
Acquired by 1874

P729

**P729    THE SOLDIER'S GRAVE**
Signed: *H.V.*
Sepia drawing 12·1 × 10·2
Acquired by 1874

P740

**P740    A SPORTSMAN**
Signed: *H. Vernet*
Water-colour 9·2 × 12·7
Acquired by 1874

**P741   A DRUMMER**
Signed: *H. Vernet*
Water-colour 8·3 × 5·7

P741

**P743   SOLDIERS FIRING**
Signed: *HV*
Water-colour 7·3 × 5·4

P743

# Arie (Adrian) de VOIS
## *c.* 1632–1680

b. Utrecht, d. Leiden; pupil of Knupfer at Utrecht, and of A. van den Tempel
at Leiden; influenced by Dou, q.v., and F. van Mieris, q.v.

**P205   RUSTIC COURTSHIP**
Signed: *AD. Vois 1656*
panel 37·5 × 26·0
A closely related composition (34 × 27) was
on the London art market in 1924.
Acquired by 1872

P205

# Cornelis de VOS
*c.* 1585–1651

b. Hulst, d. Antwerp; pupil of D. Remeeus; history and portrait painter, influenced by Rubens and van Dyck, q.v. (E. Greindl, *Corneille de Vos*, Brussels, 1944)

P18

### P18    PORTRAIT OF A MAN

Panel 123·8 × 93·3

Painted *c.* 1625. Formerly considered to be the pendant to P22 below, and possibly a portrait of Paul de Vos, the artist's younger brother. (Greindl, p. 142)

Purchased by Sir Richard Wallace 1872

P22

### P22    PORTRAIT OF A LADY

Panel 123·5 × 92·4

Painted *c.* 1622; the same interior appears in a portrait by de Vos in the John G. Johnson collection, Philadelphia (dated 1622), and in his *Salon de Rubens* (Stockholm), and probably represents the artist's own house. The stomacher worn in P22 also reappears in the Philadelphia portrait (and, apparently, in the van Dyck P16 in The Wallace Collection). Formerly thought to be the pendant to P18 above. (Greindl, pp. 142–43)

Purchased by Sir Richard Wallace 1872

# Jean-Antoine WATTEAU
## 1684–1721

b. Valenciennes, d. Nogent-sur-Marne; pupil of Gérin in Valenciennes; moved to Paris 1702 where he studied under Métayer, Gillot and Claude Audran III; visited London 1719/20; influenced by Rubens and 16th-century Venetian painting, he transmuted their baroque into a delicate, theatrical rococo. (E. Camesasca, *Opera completa di Watteau*, Milan 1968; London 1971)

**P377   THE MUSIC LESSON (Pour nous prouver que cette belle ...)**

Panel 18·4 × 23·8

Probably painted *c.* 1716; engraved by Surugue 1719 with verses (beginning as sub-title above). The lutanist recurs in P410 below, q.v. A pendant, with P377 until 1856, *Arlequin, Pierrot et Scapin*, is at Waddesdon. Several related drawings are recorded, and the composition was copied by Horace Walpole in 1736 (probably from the print). (Camesasca 154)

P377

Purchased by the 4th Marquess of Hertford 1856

**P381   GILLES AND HIS FAMILY (Sous un habit de Mezetin ...)**

Panel 27·6 × 21·3

Probably painted *c.* 1715; engraved by Thomassin *fils* with verses (beginning as sub-title above). The central figure, according to Mariette, is the dealer Sirois, shown with his family. Several related drawings are recorded. Probably pendant to *Les habits sont italiens* (version at Waddesdon; two others recorded). (Camesasca 181)

Acquired by 1872

P381

**P387   HARLEQUIN AND COLUMBINE (Voulez vous triompher des Belles ...)**

Panel 36·8 × 27·6

Probably painted *c.* 1715; engraved by Thomassin *fils* 1725 with verses (beginning as sub-title above). Several related drawings are recorded. A miniature version is in The Wallace Collection (M142). (Camesasca 152)

Acquired by (Sir) Richard Wallace by 1859

P387

P389

## P389   LES CHAMPS-ÉLYSÉES

Panel 33·0 × 42·5

Probably painted *c.* 1716; engraved by Tardieu 1727 with present title. The composition comparable with that of P391 below. Several related drawings are recorded. (Camesasca 156)

Purchased by the 4th Marquess of Hertford 1848

## P391   FÊTE IN A PARK (Divertissements champêtres)

Canvas 127·6 × 193·0

Probably painted *c.* 1719; not engraved; an enlarged and less accomplished version of P389 above. The sculpted nymph on the fountain recurs in *La leçon d'amour* (Stockholm) and *Le Bosquet de Bacchus* (engraved by Cochin 1727). Cleaned and restored 1975. Several related drawings are recorded. (Camesasca 183)

Purchased by the 4th Marquess of Hertford 1852

P391

**P410    THE MUSIC PARTY (Les Charmes de la vie)**

Canvas 68·6 × 90·5

Probably painted *c.* 1716–18; engraved by Aveline with the sub-title above. Sold in 1748 as *Vue des anciens Champs-Élysées de la galerie des Tuileries.* The standing figure on the left has been identified as the painter Wleughels (?1668–1737); the lutanist recurs in P377 above and probably plays the role of the unsuccessful lover. Several related drawings are recorded. (Camesasca 184)

Acquired by the 4th Marquess of Hertford by 1856

P410

**P416    THE HALT (Rendez-vous de chasse)**

Canvas 127·6 × 193·7

Probably painted *c.* 1719–20; engraved by Aubert 1731. It is open to doubt whether P416 was the picture mentioned by Watteau in a letter of September 1720 addressed to de Jullienne; parts of the composition derive from etchings by Testa and Callot. Since at least 1807 regarded as a pendant to P391. Several related drawings are recorded. (Camesasca 207)

Purchased by the 4th Marquess of Hertford 1865

P416

P439

### P439  LA TOILETTE

Canvas 43·8 × 36·8 extended to 46·4 × 38·7

Probably painted 1716–17; not engraved. Several related drawings are recorded. (Camesasca 175; D. Posner, *Watteau, A Lady at her Toilet*, 1973)

Acquired by 1872

# After WATTEAU

P395

### P395  THE FOUNTAIN (La Cascade)

Canvas 45·7 × 36·8

Watteau's original composition, now in a private collection in Paris, was engraved by Scotin 1729; P395 is an inferior copy. The fountain group is copied from a group by Sarrazin, once in Crozat's collection. (cf. Camesasca 133)

Acquired by 1872

P420

### P420  THE BALL (Les Plaisirs du bal)

Canvas 55·9 × 68·6

Copy of the painting at Dulwich College Gallery (53 × 66, Camesasca 164, and see Lancret P465) which was engraved by Scotin with verses beginning as sub-title above. P420 has been attributed to Pater. (Ingersoll-Smouse, *Pater*, 604)

Purchased by the 4th Marquess of Hertford 1865

# Jan WEENIX
## 1642?–1719

b. and d. Amsterdam; son and pupil of J. B. Weenix, q.v.; worked in Utrecht 1664–68, later settled in Amsterdam; court painter to the Elector Palatine Johann Wilhelm, *c.* 1702–12, painting hunting scenes and dead game for Schloss Bensberg.

### P59  FLOWERS ON A FOUNTAIN, WITH A PEACOCK

Canvas 180·3 × 168·9

Acquired by 1872

P59

### P62  WHITE COCKATOO AND OTHER BIRDS

Canvas 121·9 × 110·5

Acquired by 1872

P62

P67

**P67    RED MACAW AND OTHER BIRDS**

Canvas 121·9 × 112·4

Acquired by 1872

**P69    PEACOCK, DEAD GAME AND MONKEY**

Canvas 189·9 × 168·3

Acquired by 1872

P69

**P87 HARES AND PHEASANT AT A FOUNTAIN WITH A DOG**

Canvas 160·7 × 212·1

Purchased by the 4th Marquess of Hertford 1845

P87

**P91 DEAD GAME**

Signed: *J. Weenix f. 1691*

Canvas 91·1 × 101·9

P91

**P98 DEAD GAME AND SMALL BIRDS**

Canvas 138·4 × 174·6

Purchased by the 4th Marquess of Hertford 1867

P98

P102

## P102   FLOWERS AND FRUIT

Signed: *J. Weenix f. 1696*

Canvas 127·0 × 105·4

P103

## P103   DEAD HARE AND DOG

Signed: *J. Weenix f. 1717*

Canvas 124·8 × 107·6

P124

## P124   DEAD GOOSE AND PEACOCK

Signed: *J. Weenix f. 1718*

Canvas 174·9 × 122·2

Purchased by the 4th Marquess of Hertford 1867

**P140   DEAD PEACOCK AND GAME**

Signed: *J. Weenix f. 1707*

Canvas 116·5 × 97·8

Purchased by the 4th Marquess of Hertford 1867

P140

**P141   DEAD HARE, FRUIT AND MONKEY**

Signed: *J. Weenix f. 1704*

Canvas 120·7 × 99·1

P141

**P142   DEAD GAME WITH SPORTING DOG**

Canvas 149·9 × 127·9

P142

P174

**P174   DEAD HARE AND STILL LIFE**

Signed: *J. Weenix f. 1692*

Canvas 81·9 × 64·8

P182

**P182   DEAD HARE AND PARTRIDGES**

Signed: *J. Weenix f.*

Canvas 90·8 × 73·7

Purchased by the 4th Marquess of Hertford 1867

P233

**P233   DEAD BIRDS**

Canvas 62·9 × 49·2

# Jan Baptist WEENIX
## 1621–1660(?)

b. Amsterdam, d. Huis ter Mey; pupil of Micker and Moeyaert in Amsterdam and of A. Bloemaert in Utrecht; in Italy 1642/3–47, working in Rome for the future Pope Innocent X; settled in Utrecht 1649–57; painter of italianate port scenes and landscapes, and of still-life.

**P117   COAST SCENE WITH CLASSICAL RUINS**

Signed: *Gio. Batta Weenix 1649 16 Sep.*

Canvas 85·1 × 109·5

Jan Weenix, q.v., the painter's son, recorded that his father had several times painted a picture 6 or 7 feet wide in one day, which might have some bearing on the specific date inscribed on P117. A drawing for the central figure with the dog is in the Musée Cantini, Marseille.

Purchased by the 4th Marquess of Hertford 1843

P117

**P146   COAST SCENE WITH BUILDINGS**

Panel 28·6 × 23·2

Acquired by 1872

P146

# Adriaen van der WERFF
## 1659–1722

b. Kralingen, d. Rotterdam; pupil of Picolet and of Eglon Hendrik van der Neer, q.v., in Rotterdam where he practised nearly all his life; court painter to the Elector Palatine from 1697 and knighted 1703; also worked for the King of Poland and the Duke of Brunswick; his highly finished paintings brought him great fame and wealth.

**P151   VENUS AND CUPID**

Signed: *Chevᵣ vᵣ Werff 1716*

Panel 45·4 × 33·7

(HdG 124)

Purchased by the 4th Marquess of Hertford 1846(?)

P151

P165

**P165   SHEPHERD AND SHEPHERDESS**

Signed: *Ad$^n$ v Werff fe 1690*

Canvas 47·6 × 39·4

Two further versions are recorded, one (panel 46 × 38) at Berlin-Dahlem. (HdG 151)

Acquired by 1872

# Richard WESTALL
## 1765–1836

b. Hertford, d. London; studied in the RA schools; painter of literary and classical histories.

P566

**P566   CYMON AND IPHIGENIA**

Panel 21·6 × 26·7

Copy of the painting by Reynolds, q.v., at Buckingham Palace (143 × 172, first exhibited in 1789); the subject is taken from Boccaccio's *Decameron*.

P757

**P757   TITANIA**

Signed: *R. Westall 1793*

Water-colour 29·8 × 38·7

The subject is taken from Shakespeare's *A Midsummer Night's Dream*.

Acquired by 1872

# Jan WIJNANTS
active 1643–d. 1684

b. Haarlem, d. Amsterdam; lived in Haarlem until 1659, settled in Amsterdam 1660; painter of predominantly dune-landscapes.

**P160   LANDSCAPE WITH CATTLE**

Signed: *J. Wijnants 1661*

Canvas 63·5 × 90·5

The cattle and figures have been attributed to A. van de Velde, q.v. (HdG 361)

P160

**P190   LANDSCAPE WITH BARE TREE**

Signed: *Wijnants 1659*

Canvas 50·2 × 58·4

The figures have been attributed to Lingelbach. (HdG 314)

Purchased by the 4th Marquess of Hertford 1861

P190

**P249   A HILLY LANDSCAPE**

Signed: *J. Wijnants*

Canvas 57·5 × 50·8

The figures have been attributed to A. van de Velde, q.v. (HdG 141)

Acquired by the 4th Marquess of Hertford by 1857

P249

# David WILKIE
## 1785–1841

b. Cults, Fifeshire, d. at sea; studied at the Trustees' Academy, Edinburgh, and the RA schools, London; travelled in Italy and Spain 1825; painter to the King 1830; knighted 1836; his earlier genre subjects were succeeded by history pieces and portraiture.

P352

### P352   THE SCOTTISH BEDROOM

Signed: *D. Wilkie 1824*

Panel 29·8 × 38·1

The subject is taken from Allan Ramsay's *The Gentle Shepherd* (Glaud watching Peggy and Jenny finish dressing). Commissioned in 1823 by the Duke of Bedford. A later study (panel 20 × 24) is in a private collection.

Purchased by the 4th Marquess of Hertford 1853

P357

### P357   THE SPORTSMAN

Signed: *D. Wilkie 1824*

Panel 26·7 × 31·1

Commissioned by General Phipps (first Earl of Mulgrave); the sportsman is Col. (later Sir Charles) Phipps, the farmer's daughter is Lady Lepel Charlotte Phipps.

Purchased by the 4th Marquess of Hertford 1859

# Hermann WINTERHALTER
## 1808–1891

b. Saint-Blaise, d. Karlsruhe; brother of F. X. Winterhalter (who painted Queen Victoria); studied in Munich and Rome; portrait and genre painter.

P669

### P669   A GIRL OF FRASCATI

Signed: *H. Winterhalter*

Water-colour 23·5 × 18·7

Previously catalogued as by F. X. Winterhalter. Frascati, near Rome, where Winterhalter studied before 1840.

Acquired by 1874

# Emmanuel de WITTE
## 1615/17–1691/2

b. Alkmaar, d. Amsterdam; worked in Rotterdam 1639–40, Delft 1650–1, and Amsterdam from 1652; began as a figure painter, but specialised in church interiors from *c.* 1650.

### P254   INTERIOR OF THE OUDE KERK, DELFT

Signed: *E. De Witte A° 1651*

Panel 60·6 × 43·8

View from the south transept. Formerly in an ebony frame with shutters, as it appears in the background of a picture, attributed to B. van der Bossche, at Petworth, showing Cornelis Ploss van Amstel with four friends; P254 was sold from van Amstel's collection in 1800. A drawing by G. van der Myn in the Lugt collection, also shows the same view in Ploss van Amstel's house.

Purchased by Sir Richard Wallace 1872

P254

# Philips WOUWERMANS
## 1619–1668

b. and d. Haarlem; probably a pupil of his father (d. 1642) and Frans Hals, q.v., in Haarlem; influenced by J. Wijnants, q.v., P. Verbeecq and P. van Laer; painted some religious and historical scenes, but primarily a painter of landscapes with animals.

### P65   THE HORSE FAIR

Signed: PHILIPS (monogram) W.

Panel 66·0 × 88·9

Probably painted in the 1660s. Engraved by Moyreau 1735 as *Le grand marché aux chevaux.* (HdG 183)

Purchased by the 4th Marquess of Hertford 1854(?)

P65

P144

### P144   SHOEING A HORSE

Signed: PHILIPS (monogram) W.

Panel 34·9 × 31·1

(HdG 135, 162)

Acquired by the 4th Marquess of Hertford by 1857

P187

### P187   A CONVERSATION BY THE SEA

Signed: PHILIPS (monogram) W.

Panel 25·7 × 33·0

(HdG 1075, 993 as 'at Scheveningen')

Purchased by the 4th Marquess of Hertford 1861

P193

### P193   A CAMP SCENE

Signed: PHILIPS (monogram) W.

Panel 39·1 × 50·3

(HdG 862)

Purchased by the 3rd Marquess of Hertford 1810(?)

P216

### P216   LOADING A BOAT

Signed: PHILIPS (monogram) W.

Panel 41·3 × 36·2

(HdG 1003, 1076)

Purchased by the 4th Marquess of Hertford 1866

## P218   A STREAM IN HILLY COUNTRY

Signed: PHL *W.*

Canvas 67·6 × 58·4

(HdG 1077)

Purchased by the 4th Marquess of Hertford 1848

P218

## P226   BY THE RIVERSIDE

Signed: PHILIPS (monogram)...

Panel 42·3 × 53·3

(HdG 221, 1112)

Purchased by the 4th Marquess of Hertford 1848

P226

# Félix ZIEM
## 1821–1911

b. Beaune, d. Paris; studied at Dijon as an architect; travelled in Rome, Venice and Constantinople; first exhibited his paintings in 1849; painter of architectural views and sea-pieces.

### P366   VENICE

Signed: *Ziem*

Canvas 92·7 × 151·3

View from the mouth of the Grand Canal, with the Doge's Palace on the right, S. Maria della Salute on the left. Probably painted *c*. 1870.

Acquired by 1872

P366

# NUMERICAL INDEX

P1 Cima
P2 Bianchi Ferrari, ascribed
P3 Murillo
P4 Velazquez, after
P5 Titian, after
P6 Velazquez, after
P7 Meneses Osorio, attributed
P8 Luini
P9 Sarto
P10 Luini
P11 Titian
P12 Velazquez
P13 Murillo, after
P14 Murillo
P15 Cano
P16 Dyck, van
P17 Ostade, I. van
P18 Vos, de
P19 Titian, follower
P20 Noort
P21 Ostade, I. van, after
P22 Vos, Cornelis de
P23 Hoogh, de
P24 Both, ascribed
P25 Berchem
P26 Pourbus, F.
P27 Hoogh, de
P28 Both
P29 Rembrandt
P30 Rubens, studio
P31 Reynolds
P32 Reynolds
P33 Reynolds
P34 Murillo
P35 Reynolds
P36 Reynolds
P37 Romney
P38 Reynolds
P39 Lawrence
P40 Reynolds
P41 Lawrence
P42 Gainsborough
P43 Reynolds
P44 Gainsborough
P45 Reynolds
P46 Murillo
P47 Reynolds
P48 Reynolds
P49 Cuyp
P50 Ruisdael
P51 Cuyp
P52 Rembrandt
P53 Dyck, van, follower
P54 Cuyp
P55 Rembrandt, imitator

P56 Ruisdael
P57 Pynacker
P58 Murillo
P59 Weenix, Jan
P60 Hobbema
P61 Drost, attributed
P62 Weenix, Jan
P63 Rubens
P64 Hondecoeter
P65 Wouwermans
P66 Miereveld
P67 Weenix, Jan
P68 Murillo
P69 Weenix, Jan
P70 Velazquez, after
P71 Rubens
P72 Snijders
P73 Ostade, I. van
P74 Bol
P75 Hobbema
P76 Heem, de
P77 Velde, W. van de
P78 Bol, attributed
P79 Dyck, van
P80 Velde, A. van de
P81 Rubens
P82 Rembrandt
P83 Hondecoeter
P84 Hals
P85 Dyck, van
P86 Rembrandt, follower
P87 Weenix, Jan
P88 Velazquez
P89 Backer
P90 Rembrandt
P91 Weenix, Jan
P92 Coques
P93 Rubens
P94 Dyck, van
P95 Hobbema
P96 Noort
P97 Murillo
P98 Weenix, Jan
P99 Hobbema
P100 Velazquez, after
P101 Fyt
P102 Weenix, Jan
P103 Weenix, Jan
P104 Murillo, follower
P105 Murillo
P106 Velazquez, after
P107 Heem, de
P108 Poussin
P109 Velazquez, after
P110 Helst, van der

| | |
|---|---|
| P111 | Steen |
| P112 | Dyck, van, after |
| P113 | Everdingen |
| P114 | Claude |
| P115 | Pynacker |
| P116 | Rosa |
| P117 | Weenix, Jan Baptist |
| P118 | Dyck, van, after |
| P119 | Champaigne |
| P120 | Jordaens |
| P121 | Hackaert |
| P122 | Troy, F. de, attrib. |
| P123 | Dyck, van, after |
| P124 | Weenix, Jan |
| P125 | Claude, after |
| P126 | Sassoferrato |
| P127 | Champaigne |
| P128 | Raoux |
| P129 | Champaigne |
| P130 | Rigaud, studio |
| P131 | Domenichino |
| P132 | Camphuijsen |
| P133 | Murillo |
| P134 | Champaigne |
| P135 | Vernet, C. J. |
| P136 | Murillo, attributed |
| P137 | Velde, W. van de |
| P138 | Cuyp |
| P139 | Dughet |
| P140 | Weenix, Jan |
| P141 | Weenix, Jan |
| P142 | Weenix, Jan |
| P143 | Velde, W. van de |
| P144 | Wouwermans |
| P145 | Velde, W. van de |
| P146 | Weenix, Jan Baptist |
| P147 | Strij, attributed |
| P148 | Ruisdael, after |
| P149 | Huijsum, van |
| P150 | Steen |
| P151 | Werff, van der |
| P152 | Neefs |
| P153 | Dietrich |
| P154 | Steen |
| P155 | Mieris, W. van |
| P156 | Ruisdael |
| P157 | Neer, A. van der, after |
| P158 | Steen |
| P159 | Neer, A. van der |
| P160 | Wijnants |
| P161 | Neer, A. van der |
| P162 | Coques |
| P163 | Mieris, W. van |
| P164 | Hobbema |
| P165 | Werff, van der |
| P166 | Boursse |
| P167 | Netscher |
| P168 | Dou, after |
| P169 | Ostade, A. van |
| P170 | Dou |
| P171 | Schalcken |
| P172 | Calraert |
| P173 | Rembrandt, after |
| P174 | Weenix, Jan |
| P175 | Heem, de |
| P176 | Mieris, J. van |
| P177 | Dou |
| P178 | Mieris, W. van |
| P179 | Mieris, W. van |
| P180 | Calraert |
| P181 | Mieris, W. van |
| P182 | Weenix, Jan |
| P183 | Berchem |
| P184 | Neer, A. van der, after |
| P185 | Berchem |
| P186 | Berchem |
| P187 | Wouwermans |
| P188 | Mieris, W. van |
| P189 | Potter |
| P190 | Wijnants |
| P191 | Teniers |
| P192 | Pot |
| P193 | Wouwermans |
| P194 | Velde, W. van de |
| P195 | Heyden, van der |
| P196 | Teniers |
| P197 | Ruisdael, ascribed |
| P198 | Both |
| P199 | Velde, A. van de |
| P200 | Neer, A. van der |
| P201 | Rembrandt, follower |
| P202 | Ostade, A. van |
| P203 | Rembrandt |
| P204 | Netscher |
| P205 | Vois, de |
| P206 | Metsu |
| P207 | Huijsum, van |
| P208 | Storck, attributed |
| P209 | Steen |
| P210 | Teniers |
| P211 | Brouwer |
| P212 | Netscher |
| P213 | Berchem |
| P214 | Netscher |
| P215 | Velde, W. van de |
| P216 | Wouwermans |
| P217 | Neer, A. van der |
| P218 | Wouwermans |
| P219 | Potter |
| P220 | Mieris, W. van |
| P221 | Velde, W. van |
| P222 | Jardin, du |
| P223 | Coques |
| P224 | Maes |
| P225 | Heyden, van der |
| P226 | Wouwermans |
| P227 | Teniers |
| P228 | Calraert |
| P229 | Rembrandt |
| P230 | Heyden, van der |
| P231 | Teniers |
| P232 | Cuyp, after |
| P233 | Weenix, Jan |
| P234 | Metsu |

P235   ter Borch
P236   ter Borch
P237   Netscher
P238   Flinck
P239   Maes
P240   Metsu
P241   Jardin, du
P242   Metsu
P243   Neer, E. van der
P244   Backhuisen
P245   Hackaert
P246   Velde, W. van de
P247   Ruisdael, after
P248   Backhuisen
P249   Wijnants
P250   Cuyp, after
P251   Metsu
P252   Potter
P253   Cuyp, after
P254   Witte, de
P255   Cuyp, after
P256   Berchem
P257   Landseer
P258   Roberts
P259   Decamps
P260   Bonheur
P261   Decamps
P262   Couture
P263   Decamps
P264   Prud'hon
P265   Couture
P266   Diaz
P267   Decamps
P268   Diaz
P269   Decamps
P270   Bonington
P271   Isabey
P272   Prud'hon
P273   Bonington
P274   Géricault
P275   Leys
P276   Delaroche
P277   Vernet, H.
P278   Landelle
P279   Cogniet
P280   Vernet, H.
P281   Corot
P282   Delacroix
P283   Rousseau
P284   Scheffer
P285   Roqueplan
P286   Delaroche
P287   Meissonier
P288   Couture
P289   Meissonier
P290   Meissonier
P291   Meissonier
P292   Decamps
P293   Marilhat
P294   Decamps
P295   Prud'hon
P296   Decamps

P297   Meissonier
P298   Scheffer
P299   Dupré
P300   Delaroche
P301   Gérôme
P302   Decamps
P303   Gros
P304   Decamps
P305   Decamps
P306   Gérôme
P307   Decamps
P308   Gallait
P309   Cooper
P310   Nuyen
P311   Delaroche
P312   Diaz
P313   Prud'hon
P314   Delaroche
P315   Prud'hon
P316   Scheffer
P317   Marilhat
P318   Decamps
P319   Bonington
P320   Delaroche
P321   Scheffer
P322   Bonington
P323   Bonington
P324   Delacroix
P325   Meissonier
P326   Meissonier
P327   Meissonier
P328   Meissonier
P329   Meissonier
P330   Meissonier
P331   Meissonier
P332   Meissonier
P333   Bonington
P334   Marilhat
P335   Isabey
P336   Vernet, H.
P337   Meissonier
P338   Pettenkofen
P339   Bonington
P340   Couture
P341   Bonington
P342   Heilbuth
P343   Stanfield
P344   Troyon
P345   Decamps
P346   Vernet, H.
P347   Prud'hon
P348   Mayer
P349   Vernet, H.
P350   Decamps
P351   Bonington
P352   Wilkie
P353   Decamps
P354   Stanfield
P355   Delaroche
P356   Marilhat
P357   Wilkie
P358   Delaroche

P359   Troyon
P360   Isabey
P361   Robert-Fleury
P362   Bonington
P363   Brascassat
P364   Bonheur
P365   Bonheur
P366   Ziem
P367   Vernet, H.
P368   Vernet, H.
P369   Meissonier
P370   Couture
P371   Meissonier
P372   Bonheur
P373   Landseer
P374   Fauvelet
P375   Bonington
P376   Landseer
P377   Watteau
P378   Lancret
P379   Fragonard
P380   Pater
P381   Watteau
P382   Fragonard
P383   Pater
P384   Greuze
P385   Boucher
P386   Pater
P387   Watteau
P388   Greuze
P389   Watteau
P390   Boucher
P391   Watteau
P392   Lemoyne
P363   Lancret
P394   Fragonard
P395   Watteau, after
P396   Greuze
P397   Pater
P398   Greuze
P399   Boucher
P400   Pater
P401   Lancret
P402   Greuze
P403   Greuze
P404   Fragonard
P405   Pater
P406   Pater
P407   Greuze
P408   Lancret
P409   Lancret
P410   Watteau
P411   Boucher
P412   Fragonard
P413   Greuze
P414   Nattier, after
P415   Greuze
P416   Watteau
P417   Lemoyne
P418   Boucher
P419   Greuze
P420   Watteau, after

P421   Greuze
P422   Lancret
P423   Boucher
P424   Pater
P425   Greuze
P426   Pater
P427   Greuze
P428   Greuze
P429   Boucher
P430   Fragonard
P431   Boucher
P432   Boucher
P433   Boucher
P434   Greuze
P435   Boilly
P436   Lancret
P437   Nattier, after
P438   Boucher
P439   Watteau
P440   Greuze
P441   Greuze
P442   Greuze
P443   Greuze
P444   Boucher
P445   Boucher
P446   Boucher
P447   Boucher
P448   Lancret
P449   Lebrun
P450   Lancret
P451   Loo, C. A. van
P452   Pater
P453   Nattier
P454   Greuze
P455   Fragonard
P456   Nattier
P457   Lebrun
P458   Pater
P459   Greuze
P460   Pater
P461   Nattier
P462   Marne, de
P463   Troy, J. F. de
P464   Lépicié
P465   Lancret
P466   Lépicié
P467   Boucher, after
P468   Boucher, after
P469   Marne, de
P470   Troy, J. F. de
P471   Fragonard
P472   Pater
P473   Boilly
P474   Charlier
P475   Charlier
P476   Charlier
P477   Loo, L-M. van
P478   Lancret
P479   Boilly
P480   Vernet, C. J.
P481   Boucher
P482   Boucher

P483  Fragonard
P484  Boucher
P485  Boucher
P486  Boucher
P487  Boucher
P488  Fragonard
P489  Boucher
P490  Boucher
P491  Guardi
P492  Canaletto, studio
P493  Italian school
P494  Guardi
P495  Canaletto, imitator
P496  Canaletto
P497  Canaletto
P498  Venetian school
P499  Canaletto
P500  Canaletto, studio
P501  Canaletto, imitator
P502  Guardi
P503  Guardi
P504  Guardi
P505  Canaletto, studio
P506  Canaletto, studio
P507  Canaletto
P508  Guardi
P509  Canaletto
P510  Canaletto, studio
P511  Canaletto
P512  Canaletto, imitator
P513  Venetian school
P514  Canaletto
P515  Canaletto, imitator
P516  Canaletto
P517  Guardi
P518  Guardi
P519  Rubens
P520  Rubens
P521  Rubens
P522  Rubens
P523  Rubens
P524  Rubens
P525  Beccafumi, attributed
P526  Luini
P527  Crivelli
P528  Memlinc
P529  Flemish
P530  Clouet, after
P531  Pourbus, P.
P532  Corneille de Lyon, workshop
P533  German
P534  Meulen, van der, attrib.
P535  Eworth, follower
P536  Ferrarese school
P537  Luini
P538  Foppa
P539  Bonsignòri, attributed
P540  Umbrian school
P541  North Italian
P542  North Italian
P543  Benvenuto di Giovanni, attrib.
P544  Milanese school

P545  Spagna, Lo
P546  Titian, after
P547  Holbein, after
P548  Master of the Magdalen Legend, after
P549  Daddi, follower
P550  Francesco di Vanuccio
P551  Cleve, van, after
P552  Parma, school
P553  Roman school
P554  Holbein, after
P555  Bronzino, after
P556  Florentine school
P557  Angeli, von
P558  Lawrence
P559  Lawrence
P560  Ramsay, after
P561  Reynolds
P562  Dolci
P563  Hoppner
P564  Sully
P565  Sassoferrato
P566  Westall
P567  Papety
P568  Schopin
P569  Saint-Jean
P570  Leys
P571  Roqueplan
P572  Vernet, H.
P573  Schelfhout
P574  Morland
P575  Vernet, H.
P576  Heilbuth
P577  Vernet, H.
P578  Symonds
P579  Isabey
P580  Gudin
P581  Bellangé
P582  Vernet, H.
P583  Roqueplan
P584  Vernet, H.
P585  Vernet, H.
P586  Bellangé
P587  Roberts
P588  Calame
P589  Landseer
P590  Robert
P591  Robert
P592  Robert
P593  Vernet, H.
P594  Desportes
P595  Roqueplan
P596  Delaroche
P597  Merle
P598  Vernet, H.
P599  French school
P600  Papety
P601  Saint-Jean
P602  Sant
P603  Roqueplan
P604  Delaroche
P605  Muller
P606  Vernet, H.

P607    Vernet, H.
P608    Vernet, H.
P609    Roqueplan
P610    Vernet, H.
P611    Papety
P612    Roqueplan
P613    Vernet, H.
P614    Vernet, H.
P615    Robert
P616    Scheffer
P617    Newton
P618    Achenbach
P619    Vernet, H.
P620    Bellangé
P621    Pettenkofen, after
P622    Verboeckhoven
P623    Desportes
P624    Oudry
P625    Oudry
P626    Oudry
P627    Oudry
P628    Desportes
P629    Oudry
P630    Oudry
P631    Oudry
P632    Morton
P633    Hilton
P634    Platzer
P635    Teniers
P636    Teniers
P637    Teniers
P638    Teniers
P639    Mieris, F. van
P640    Berchem
P641    Jardin, du
P642    Albani
P643    Bilivert, after
P644    Reni, after
P645    Champaigne, after
P646    Sassoferrato
P647    Guardi
P648    Jacquand
P649    Decamps
P650    Bellangé
P651    Turner
P652    Roqueplan
P653    Lami
P654    Turner
P655    Decamps
P656    Bonington
P657    Bonington
P658    Harding, J. D.
P659    Roberts
P660    Decamps
P661    Turner
P662    Roqueplan
P663    Lami
P664    Turner
P665    Pils
P666    Decamps
P667    Stanfield
P668    Bonington

P669    Winterhalter
P670    Decamps
P671    Bellangé
P672    Bonington
P673    Papety
P674    Bonington
P675    Bonington
P676    Bonington
P677    Decamps
P678    Bonington
P679    Bonington
P680    Roberts
P681    Cogniet
P682    Decamps
P683    Bellangé
P684    Bonington
P685    Cogniet
P686    Robert-Fleury
P687    Scheffer
P688    Bonington
P689    Roberts
P690    Fielding
P691    Fielding
P692    Decamps
P693    Johannot
P694    Harper
P695    Harper
P696    Bonington
P697    Roberts
P698    Bonington
P699    Decamps
P700    Bonington
P701    Bonington
P702    Lami
P703    Nesfield
P704    Bonington
P705    Bellangé
P706    Decamps
P707    Roqueplan
P708    Bonington
P709    Derby
P710    Lami
P711    Papety
P712    Stanfield
P713    Derby
P714    Bonington
P715    Fielding
P716    Fielding
P717    Decamps
P718    Fielding
P719    Vernet, H.
P720    Bellangé
P721    Brascassat
P722    Decamps
P723    Lami
P724    Vernet, H.
P725    Derby
P726    Bonington
P727    Bonington
P728    Vernet, H.
P729    Vernet, H.
P730    Bellangé

P731  Raffet
P732  Bonington
P733  Bonington
P734  Bonington
P735  Delaroche
P736  Hove, van
P737  Raffet
P738  Delaroche
P739  Johannot
P740  Vernet, H.
P741  Vernet, H.
P742  Bellangé
P743  Vernet, H.
P744  Raffet
P745  Raffet
P746  Callow
P747  Raffet
P748  Bellangé
P749  Bonington
P750  Bonington
P751  Downman
P752  Downman
P753  Downman
P754  Downman

P755  Géricault
P756  Ostade, A. van, after
P757  Westall
P760  Saint-Jean
P761  Saint-Jean
P762  Pollaiuolo, after
P763  Mirbel
P764  Mirbel
P765  Denning
P766  Boucher, follower
P767  Ingres
P768  Florentine school
P769  Courtois
P770  Harding, S.
P771  Hondius
P772  Lafrensen
P773  Netscher (see P237)
P774  Maratti, attributed
P775  Polidoro
P776  Boucher, follower
P777  Rembrandt (see P203)
P778  Robert-Fleury
P780  Saint-Aubin

## ATTRIBUTIONS RENAMED SINCE 1968

| 1968 | no. | 1978 |
|---|---|---|
| School of MURILLO | P7 | Attributed to MENESES Osorio |
| G. FLINCK | P78 | Attributed to F. BOL |
| P. de RING | P107 | J. D. de HEEM |
| N. de LARGILLIERRE | P122 | Attributed to F. de TROY |
| FLEMISH or GERMAN school | P534 | Attributed to S. van der MEULEN |
| F. X. WINTERHALTER | P669 | H. WINTERHALTER |

# Appendix

The following pictures are also at Hertford House, but were not part of Lady Wallace's Bequest; they are not, therefore, part of The Wallace Collection.

## François BOUCHER
### 1703–1770 q.v.

**PA1  A TRITON**

Black chalk 21·6 × 26·7

Study for the triton which appears in *The Rising of The Sun* (P485, bottom left), q.v. (Ananoff 422/7)

Presented to the Library by the National Art-Collections Fund 1941

PA1

## Ferdinand-Victor-Eugène DELACROIX
### 1798–1863 q.v.

**PA2  STUDIES OF ARMOUR FROM THE MEYRICK COLLECTION**

Black lead 19·1 × 27·9

Stamped *E.D.* (indicating it was included in the artist's sale of 1864) and annotated by the artist; showing, from the left: a suit of 16th-century English armour (now A62 in The Wallace Collection); two studies of a suit of 16th-century German armour (now at Warwick Castle), and a suit of 16th-century German armour (now A26 and A448 in The Wallace Collection). Delacroix visited Dr. (Sir Samuel) Meyrick's collection in Cadogan Place, London, on 8 July 1825 with Bertin and, possibly, Bonington to whom this drawing was attributed until 1964. (Exhibited: *Delacroix*, RA 1964 (95); *Bonington*, Nottingham 1965 (340)).

Presented to the Library by Sir James Mann 1954

PA2

# Henry EDRIDGE
1769–1821

PA3

**PA3  ISABELLA, 2nd MARCHIONESS OF HERTFORD**

Black lead 17·1 × 12·7

Inscribed, verso, as the Viscountess Beauchamp, later 2nd Marchioness, probably indicating a date before 1794. See Downman P751.

Purchased for the Library 1960

# ENGLISH
mid-19th century

PA4

**TWO STUDIES OF ARMOUR FROM THE HOHENASCHAU COLLECTION**

**PA4**  Black lead 22·1 × 19·6 a close helmet and half armour, now A54 and A164 in the Wallace Collection

**PA5**  Black lead 24·8 × 20·5 a suit of equestrian armour, now in the Metropolitan Museum, New York.

Drawn before c. 1860 when the collection was dispersed. Previously tentatively attributed to G. P. Harding.

Presented to the Library by Sir James Mann 1954

PA5

# Richard, 4th Marquess of HERTFORD, ascribed to
## 1800–1870

### TWO STUDIES OF HUSSARS ON HORSE-BACK

**PA6**   Water-colour 16·3 × 22·6
**PA7**   Water-colour 14·7 × 22·6

Uniforms are those of the 8th and 15th Hussars; the 4th Marquess was a serving member of the 10th Hussars 1820–23. Acquired from the descendants of Sir John Murray Scott (see PA8 below) as by the 4th Marquess, but the attribution is open to doubt.

Presented to the Library by Mr. Burton Jones 1943

PA6

PA7

# Herman G. HERKOMER
## 1863–1935

### PA8   SIR JOHN MURRAY SCOTT

Signed: *Herman G Herkomer 190[9?]*

Canvas 127·0 × 101·6

Sir John Murray Scott (1843–1913), secretary to Sir Richard Wallace, confidential adviser and residuary legatee of Lady Wallace, and Trustee of the Wallace Collection.

Presented to the Library by the Misses Scott 1919

PA8